KELLER BRELAND

MARIAN BRELAND

ANIMAL
BEHAVIOR

The Macmillan Company, New York
Collier-Macmillan Limited, London

TO OUR CHILDREN

Bradley, Frances, and Beth

Foreword

The Critical Issues in Psychology Series, paperback source books for the undergraduate in psychology, are designed to provide authoritative and provocative reviews of selected topics germane to a spectrum of courses. Each volume offers an original inquiry into major facets of the point at issue and a set of illuminating reports carefully chosen to represent salient positions of historical or current significance. It is expected that this combination will afford instructor and student opportunity to read stimulating, even challenging, argument with primary sources in hand.

The study of animal behavior has long been a favorite activity of laymen as well as scientists. The scientific study has been marked in recent years by an increasingly productive rapprochement of the field observation of the biologist, usually called an ethologist, and the laboratory experiment of the psychologist. This book represents something of a similar rapprochement, because the authors were trained in the psychology laboratory (under B. F. Skinner) but have done their own research and development more or less in the field.

The late Keller Breland and his wife Marian have been unique among psychologists in that they applied their scientific training in animal behavior to a vigorous, successful commercial venture. Their company, Animal Behavior Enterprises, operating out of Hot Springs, Arkansas, is a major source of trained domestic animals used in various kinds of public demonstrations as well as on television shows. Until his recent (1965) untimely death, Keller Breland served as president of this company, with Marian Breland as business manager and partner. Their many years of close observation of thousands of trained animals help make their account, as well as their interpretations and speculations, most absorbing.

MELVIN H. MARX, *General Editor*

Preface

DURING THE YEARS OF OUR WORK ON THIS BOOK (AND I
mean *years* literally, although we began actual preparation of the manuscript in 1964), it has been our hope that at the very least it would be,
like almost everything else we have done, a little bit different. We have
hoped that it would be controversial—that it would arouse interest, inspire
debate, stimulate further reading, provide ideas for research. This inspiration to creativity, and the championing of undespairing independent
thought, may well be our chief legacy to the world.

The manuscript was virtually completed at the time of my husband's
death. After consultation with the editors and with friends who read the
rough draft, there have been some editorial changes—mostly minor,
although some have perhaps been rather substantial. For these I must
take full responsibility—credit or blame. I would also like to emphasize
that Mr. Breland was always the principal author; his were the ideas,
the creative spark, and the bulk of the substantive portion of the writing.
I have been the journalist, organizer, rewrite editor, and author of nar-
ration and expository prose. Another way of putting it might be to say
that he was the architect of the dreams and I the engineer. It is my hope,
of course, that the spark and the dreams may stay alive and grow, even
perhaps partially through this book.

I would like to thank Dr. Melvin H. Marx, editor of the series, for his
general help throughout the preparation of the book and for his detailed

comments. I am also greatly indebted to Dr. Hardy Wilcoxon, University of Arkansas, Mr. F. G. Wood, Jr., Naval Missile Center, Pt. Mugu, California, Dr. Klaus Grossman, University of Freiburg, Germany, and to many members of our staff, particularly Mr. Grant Evans, our technical director, for his long creative interaction on all aspects of this endeavor, both theoretical and practical, and for his many contributions to the substance of what we have done and what we have to say; to Mr. Robert E. Bailey, assistant technical director, for his valued assistance in reading and commenting on the manuscript and providing many helpful suggestions, items of biological information, and useful references; and to Mr. Robert Garner, our training director, whose many adventures and misadventures with the animals and observations concerning them have provided much of the meat of the book. Many thanks also are due to Mrs. Helen Martin and Mrs. Myrna Garner, who have spent long hours working over the manuscript and who both have contributed much more than their considerable secretarial skills.

MARIAN BRELAND

Hot Springs, Arkansas

Contents

PART TWO: The Selected Readings

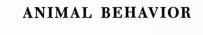

ANIMAL BEHAVIOR

PART ONE

Inquiry and Argument

CHAPTER I

A Backward Look at the Study of Animal Behavior

THE WHY

EVERY COMMERCIAL PHOTOGRAPHER AND ADVERTISER knows that the Big Three in human interest pictures are a baby, a pretty girl, and an animal. This bit of applied psychology is freely used in the pictorial media, both for advertising and entertainment. With the exception of his interest in other people, it is probably safe to say that man is more interested in animals and their behavior than anything else in his environment, and it is not too difficult to see why this should be so. Man is himself an animal, and these subhuman species are therefore his "cousins." However individual men may feel about the theory of evolution (and there are some men who have never heard of the theory of evolution and others who reject it for religious and other reasons), almost all men, whatever their condition of civilization or sophistication, recognize that the behavior of animals is the closest thing to the behavior of people that a man can encounter. In animal behavior man can see a close approximation to his own actions, emotions, and needs—in fact, sometimes, too close. In these "close calls" we sometimes get a sense of embarrassment— as when we see in the antics of monkeys traits and habits that are all too human! Sometimes we fall into the dangerous pit of anthropomorphism (which means literally "formed like a man"), or the tendency to think of animals as if they were human. Examples of such thinking can be seen around us daily—a basset hound looks sad, but the only evidence is drooping ears, red eyes, and sagging jowls. The mocking bird sounds happy when he sings (but usually he is only warning other male birds away from his nesting territory). There are many amusing examples of anthropomorphic thinking in literature about animals, and later on we will see a few of these when we see how animals have been studied in the past.

In all probability there was a time when early man was primarily a vegetarian. Teeth and jaws of some very primitive men show even greater adaptation to vegetarian life than is found in modern man (Coon, 1962), and often marks of chewing heavy roots and stems can be found rather plainly in such bony structures. In these ancient times, man had very little close association with animals except perhaps to compete with some of the vegetarian animals for foodstuffs and to fear the large predators, particularly where his children were concerned.

However, it was not too long in terms of archaeological time before certain species or races of early man apparently began to vary their vegetarian diet with grubs, small slow-moving animals, or the young of other species. These were often picked up in passing as man wandered through the brush gathering berries, nuts, and roots. The first eating of such creatures might have occurred almost by accident. It is particularly easy to see how this could happen in the case of grubs, snails, and the like. They would be almost a part of the vegetable matter on which man would be feeding. Bird eggs may also physically resemble berries and fruits, and it is not too far a step from the eating of eggs to the eating of the young birds in the nest. When man began to vary his diet in this fashion, he became even more interested in animals, and began to note their daily habits and nesting places, where eggs and the young might be found.

When man became a true hunter and added to his diet the flesh of the large animals he had to pursue, his interest in animals really developed. Then he naturally became interested in the habits of the animals upon whom he preyed. Also it was during this period of time that first the dog and later the horse were domesticated. There are many speculations about the probable domestication of the dog, but we think it is highly likely that small puppies were brought home one day by a hunter, perhaps even with the idea of eating them later. However, mamma and the children found what engaging little things they were; womankind's love for anything young in this case generalized to the puppies, and the pups responded in kind to the children's playfulness; thus they were allowed to become part of the family. But in the long run, it was the dog's fine social and pack behavior that gave him a permanent place in the home, when man learned that the dog would accept the man as the pack leader and would be a powerful tool in helping track down the large animals that were not so easy to come by as man would like. Similarly, the horse with his speed and endurance enabled man to chase down larger animals than he could readily catch on foot and also to journey long distances that on his own two feet were impossible (Dembeck, 1965).

Although the domestication of the dog and the horse may date back to the days of man as a hunter, the domestication of other animals—cats, chickens, pigs, cattle, and so on—awaited the development of agriculture and the more permanently settled family. But once man had acquired such creatures, it was, of course, important for him to learn what he could about them, their habits, and how to control them. Starting with wild species similar to man's present domestic animals, man over a period of centuries bred his animals not only for their physical characteristics—beefiness, tendency to continue laying eggs past normal nesting season, exaggeration of the milk-producing capacity, exaggerated length of wool in such animals as the sheep, and so on—but also, and perhaps most important for the true domestication process, he bred out many of the characteristics of the wild animal—the fierce aggressiveness, the tendency to attack and to flee, as well as the speed with which the animal can escape. Thus the modern domestic cattle are much more stable and slower creatures than the wild cattle from which they sprang. They are not so apt to take off across the plains at the slightest provocation, nor are the bulls as aggressive as wild bulls. The domestic cat, who dates to the early agricultural days of granaries and food storage, shows dramatically how aggressions have been bred out of a wild species.

So we see that primitive man and early historical man had many reasons to be interested in what animals were all about and why they behaved as they did.

From the viewpoint of modern man, we can make the obvious observation that research with animals is more convenient, cheaper, and has fewer ethical considerations than research performed on human beings. Just as the studies of animals in physiology, neurology, biochemistry, anatomy, and medicine have been fruitful tools for the understanding and amelioration of man's own condition, we can expect that behavioral studies will be equally fruitful, especially when interpreted in the light of some of the problems and variables we will discuss in subsequent chapters. Also from the human standpoint there are certain practical uses of the study of animal behavior —controlling animals for work of various sorts (for example, the horse and the elephant), handling and enjoyment of pets, use of animals for advertising and entertainment, and, of course, pest control. From the animal's standpoint, man's knowledge of animal behavior as applied to fish and wildlife can be of assistance to wild animal populations. Furthermore, such knowledge can help animals in any area where they interact with man, the condition of domestic animals, exhibition of animals in zoos and public entertainment, and in general in any area where the life of an animal touches the life of man.

THE HOW

We find throughout history that how man viewed the nature of his animals, his attitudes, and his methods of study have been heavily determined by his preconceived notions of what animals and their behavior are all about. Of course, we have no notion of man's preconceptions about animals in prehistoric times except those that are handed down in folklore and early religious writings. We know that many such conceptions from early history and prehistory were heavily anthropomorphic. The thinking, talking, scheming animals of Aesop's fables demonstrate this vividly. We also know that animals figured prominently in many primitive religions and were often credited with magical powers, sometimes being worshiped as gods, sometimes being assumed to be the recipients of the souls of the departed humans.

First and foremost of the writers of historic times, Aristotle tried to bring together what had previously been gathered of animal lore and in many of his writings added his own observations. His was the first scientific look at animal behavior, and although it lacks much in rigor in comparison with the methods used by the modern field naturalist and experimentalist, it is in sharp contrast to the fable, the story, and the word-of-mouth legend. He believed thoroughly in observation, and his viewpoint was wide-ranging and truly comparative.

Although Aristotle did rely rather heavily on anecdotes—little stories and observations of animal life reported often by uncritical and untrained observers—his writings are a model of decorum compared to those of Pliny (a Latin writer, A.D. 23–79). Two or three short quotations from Pliny (H. Rackham, tr., 1947) will suffice to illustrate the anecdotal method in its extreme.

The largest land animal is the elephant and is the nearest to man in intelligence; it understands the language of its country and obeys orders, remembers duties that it has been taught, is pleased by affection and by marks of honour, nay more it possesses virtues rare even in man, honesty, wisdom, justice, also respect for the stars and reverence for the sun and moon. Authorities state that in the forests of Mauretania, when the new moon is shining, herds of elephants go down to a river named Amilo and there perform a ritual of purification, sprinkling themselves with water and after thus paying their respects to the moon return to the woods carrying before them those of their calves who are tired. They are also believed to understand the obligations of another's religion in so far as to refuse to embark on board ships when going overseas before they are lured on by the mahout's sworn promise in regard to their return and they have been seen when exhausted by suffering (as even those vast frames are attacked by diseases) to lie on their backs and throw grass up to the heaven, as though deputing the earth to support their prayers. Indeed so far as concerns docility, they do homage to their king by kneeling before him and proffering garlands. The Indians employ the smaller breed which they call the bastard elephant, for ploughing. (Book VIII, page 3)

Tailed species (of apes) have even been known to play at draughts, are able to distinguish at a glance sham nuts made of wax and are depressed by the moon waning and worship the new moon with delight. (Book LXXX, page 151)

The anecdotal method is not unknown even in modern times and shortly we will see some nineteenth-century examples.

Another important philosopher of later years, who, it is true, had less to say directly about animals themselves but who nonetheless had a prominent influence in casting the form of modern science, was René Descartes, a French philosopher (1596–1650). Descartes' notion that the animal was a machine, subject to an inflexible in-line mechanistic causation has been a pervading influence in most modern psychology and physiology, particularly the American behavioristic schools. Aside from flexible speech and the influence of the human soul—whose interaction with the body Descartes thoughtfully placed in the pineal gland, thereby "taking care" of the free will problem—Descartes could see no difference between animals and machines. The animal, like the machine, was an automaton; prod it with a stimulus and it would respond, according to Descartes. External stimuli were the causes of behavior (Descartes, in *Great Books*, 1952). In fact, Descartes for better or for worse has profoundly shaped the notions, the form, and to a large extent even the strategy of all modern science. There are beginning to be hints in many fields of science, including the physical sciences, that these notions of mechanism and push-pull causation are in need of reconceptualization, and we will see later on how this situation is changing in the behavioral sciences.

In more recent times the outstanding influence on the study of animal behavior has come from the work of Darwin (1859) and his followers. By postulating the essential continuity of man with lower animals not only in their physical structure and physiology, but also their behavioral, emotional, and intellectual development, Darwin became the prime mover in instigating the scientific and systematic study of the behavior of animal species. Although pre-Darwinian biologists had begun the systematic experimental study of animal behavior, the philosophical and doctrinal questions raised by Darwin's viewpoints virtually forced its massive scientific examination. However, the actual development of a thorough natural history method followed a period of much speculation, collection of anecdotes, spinning of theories, and assembling of scientifically disreputable or dubious collections of material on animal behavior.

One perhaps unfortunate influence of the tremendous interest in the

close relationship between man and the lower animals was the humanizing tendency demonstrated by the anthropomorphic, anecdotal
school of Romanes and others. Although much more sophisticated
and more carefully selected with regard to sources, the anecdotes related by Romanes suffer from the same fundamental weak-
nesses as those of the older, more simple-minded, and less critically
selected tales of the ancients: the risk that the untrained observer
cannot give an accurate account of what he saw or that he may omit
vital information (as we shall see even a sophisticated scientist may
"fall in the soup" when he tries to describe what the animal is
doing); the confusion of interpretation of the facts; the reporting of
an incident as an event cut off from related material, including past
history and background of the animal; the tendency to report highly
selected atypical behavior; errors of memory and transmission; and
finally the difficulty of selecting reliable authentic material. An example of Romanes' material follows:

Mr. Darwin, in his "Descent of Man," gives the following account of
the exhibition of Reason on the part of a Crab:—"Mr. Gardner, whilst
watching a shore crab (gelasimus) making its burrow, threw some shells
towards the hole. One rolled in, and three other shells remained within
a few inches of the mouth. In about five minutes the crab brought out
the shell which had fallen in, and carried it away to the distance of a
foot; it then saw the three other shells lying near, and evidently thinking
that they might likewise roll in, carried them to the spot where it had
laid the first. It would, I think, be difficult to distinguish this act from
one performed by man in the aid of reason." (Romanes, 1884)

It was not until 1890 that we come to a full-fledged development
of the scientific study of animal behavior when we begin to encounter such pioneers as Sir John Lubbock, the English naturalist
(1834–1913), who seems to have been the founder of the modern
laboratory study and the originator of the maze and of the puzzle
device. Jacques Loeb (1859–1924) and Max Verworn (1863–1921)
did pioneer work on insects and unicellular animals, but perhaps
most influential of all for the future shaping of the philosophy of the
science was C. Lloyd Morgan (1852–1936), who attempted to make
a clean break between natural history methods and the older, sloppy
anecdotal style, to remove the humanizing from the studies of animals, and to study them objectively for their own sake. His famous

"Canon" (Morgan, 1894)—"In no case may we interpret an action as the outcome of the exercise of a higher psychical faculty if it can be interpreted as the outcome of the exercise of one that stands lower in the psychological scale"—is the famous philosophical and methodological dictum that served to put the brakes on much rash speculation and sentimental humanizing.

Thus at approximately the turn of the century we come to the genuine beginnings of the systematic scientific study of animal behavior. For a more detailed exposition of this development, the reader may want to refer to Volume I of Warden, Jenkins, and Warner (1935). Because this is not intended to be a detailed history of the study of animal behavior, we will leave history, returning to it at points with reference to the reading selections, to glance at the modern overviews of animal life and behavior.

Modern methods of studying animals reflect not only the holdover from older, less critical times but particularly, of course, the historical development of the methods of scientific study. Animals are still studied by man-on-the-street observation, and anecdotes can be found liberally sprinkled through popular magazines. Simple observational methods are used daily by pet owners and farmers with varying results, depending on the care with which the observations are made and the sophistication of the observer. Quite apart from this sort of observation are those of the skilled naturalists—such as Fabre [1] [1] (1823–1915). The naturalist is a trained observer who knows his animal and who is careful to report all the relevant details (and some perhaps that are not relevant). However, even the reporting of the skilled naturalist, where it is not possible to control the variables under consideration, can be subject to error, especially of interpretation, and Fabre has been criticized on this ground. He observed and wrote from a strong philosophical anti-Darwinian standpoint, and his eagerness to demonstrate the essential simplicity of the lower animals as compared to man and the higher animals may in some cases have colored his judgment and even his reporting of what he observed.

However, although it is important to be aware of the hazards involved in any method, there is no need to reject the observational methods of the skilled naturalist. In fact, they are extremely impor-

[1] Bracketed numbers refer to readings in Part Two.

tant sources of information, particularly concerning large animals that cannot be readily studied in the laboratory and large groups of animals under naturalistic conditions. In general, they are the source of a vast lore that can be accumulated only by seeing the animal as he really lives.

The laboratory method, although making it possible to control variables, of course, suffers from the inverse problem: one inevitably sacrifices some of the naturalness of the situation, and one's results may be colored by this fact.

Midway among systematic animal studies (which have been carried out under the banner of many modern scientific disciplines—zoology, genetics, physiology, neurology, biochemistry, psychology, comparative anatomy)—lies the work of the ethologists. (See reading [4].) In the early days of this discipline these were primarily European zoologists, who were concerned with controlled behavioral observations of animals in natural, or virtually natural, conditions, where variables are altered in free situations resembling as closely as possible the conditions of the animal in the wild.

Most laboratory experiments of animal behavior have been conducted by psychologists and zoologists. However, although there has been a tendency during the past half century to divide the study of animal behavior rather rigidly into departments where psychology knew not what zoology did, there are good indications that this tendency is beginning to change, and we can expect continued breakdown of departmental lines and cooperation between disciplines. Excellent studies of animal behavior are being done in animal husbandry and similar departments, and psychology students need to be aware of these (Hafez, 1962).

After this brief introduction, we can now have a look at the subject matter itself. First, however, a word on style and viewpoint might be in order. There are many books (and will be many more) which summarize the literature on animal behavior and present good reading selections from the typical experimental literature. There seems to be little reason to go over this ground here. Much of what we have to say is unique, both when we speak of our own experience and of the theory which has grown out of this experience. A good deal of the material reporting on our work is observational rather than experimental—some of the explanations and portions of the theory are frankly speculative. However, this theoretical out-look helps in understanding and prediction, and although it may prove wrong in detail, something like it, we feel sure, will turn out to be right in principle.

Secondly, we have tried to write a readable book. Sometimes we have resorted to colloquialisms and metaphor where these would eliminate the need for clumsy circumlocutions and stodgy, heavy journalese. We have endeavored to define terms as we went along, rather than resort to a glossary at the end. Some of these rather col-loquial and breezy expressions may convey from time to time an anthropomorphic or teleological bias, and we would like to set our readers straight on these matters now. Later we will see that it is virtually impossible to describe the actions of an animal without *some* human bias—a dash of anthropomorphism seems to be inevi-table, simply because we are human and must see animals through human eyes and human experiences. However, we are thoroughly aware of the dangers of ascribing complex human motives and traits to animals. Probably more than most experimenters, we are able to see animals as animals and to interpret their behavior in the light of their own life systems. Hence expressions that may seem anthropo-morphic are so only for stylistic reasons.

Similarly for teleology (the conception of natural processes as being determined by final "causes" or "purposes") we would like once and for all to state that expressions in the following that might be so interpreted are simply expressions—phrases such as *shaped by evolution* and *nature's design* are used where it seemed indicated to avoid clumsy phrases and elaborate "writing around." There is no intent to convey a belief in final causes, purposive design, or the like. Although we feel there may be a *pattern* to evolution (as is evidenced by convergent evolution itself—the tendency for animals who occupy similar environments, though widely separated in rela-tionship, to develop similar structures and appearances), this does not imply belief in a guiding purpose directing the formation of that pattern.

The vantage point from which we will take our look at animal behavior is basically that of natural science. It has been built up from laboratory science, ethological and naturalistic experiment and observation, and from the unique practical background we have had in the past eighteen years in the control of animal behavior for commercial applications. Over eight thousand animals representing more than sixty species have passed under our scrutiny; we have taught them many things, but they have taught us much more.

CHAPTER II

The Basic Nature of Behavior

You are sitting beside a stream, deep in the woods, resting your back against a tree. You have been there for some time, sitting very quietly. Now dusk is approaching, and the daytime sounds of the forest are subsiding. As you watch the stream bank, a raccoon climbs down from the rocks on the far side and begins to amble along the shore line. He stops, turns over a rock with his forepaws, moves on, and glances to one side into the bushes and briefly across the stream in your direction. He continues his shambling pace along the stream, stopping now and then to move objects on the sand. He goes down to the water line, reaches quickly into the shallow water with his forepaws, looking back over his shoulder as he does so. When he pulls his paws back out of the water, you see he holds a small object which in the fading light you can barely make out as a crayfish. He rubs the crayfish, eats it, then proceeds again, ambling along the bank. Suddenly behind you there is a distant crashing of the underbrush. The raccoon stops, looks in the direction of the sound. He stands very still. The crashing becomes louder and closer, and in an instant a large, panting dog charges out very close to your tree and stands sniffing back and forth and looking across the stream. At this point the raccoon turns tail and swiftly makes his way up a large tree above the stream.

The scene shifts; you are in a room in a modern building, looking through a one-way glass at a laboratory experiment being conducted in a closed compartment. The experimenter pushes a button; a metal coin drops into a tray. At the clinking sound, the raccoon turns toward the tray, walks over to it, picks the coin up in his paws, and turns toward a metal box with a slot in the top. The raccoon starts to put the coin in the slot, pauses; still holding the coin in his paw, he rubs it around the edge of the slot several times and finally lets it go. As it drops through the slot, an electric feeder sounds and then dispenses a piece of food. The raccoon turns to the feeder, picks up the food, and eats it.

If you are interested in animals, you may well ask yourself some questions at this point. In both scenes, what was the raccoon doing and why? In fact, what is a raccoon, really? How is he different from the dog? What is a dog, anyway? What, after all, is an animal? These sound like simple, childish questions, but they are the most fundamental ones that can be asked.

From the conventional viewpoint of the modern behavioral scientist, the analysis of what is going on, what the animal is, and what it is doing would stop with the observational facts as reported. Generally speaking, psychologists in this country (and elsewhere also) study only the gross observable behavior of the animal. In other words, they stop when the raccoon swallows the crayfish or eats the pellet of food he receives in the experiment, and in further study they simply wait for the recycling or recurrence of the behavior (the next hunt for the crayfish or the next drop of the coin and subsequent handling of it to get the next pellet of food). However, it is obvious that if the process stopped here, the animal would expire. The processes of digestion and assimilation must take over here and continue with the nourishment of the raccoon's body.

As everyone knows, animals are made up of cells, cells are made up of molecules, and the molecules, in turn, are made up of atoms and subatomic particles. Now a complex molecular structure is always subject to disintegration; left to itself, it will sooner or later spontaneously come apart. It must, therefore, be rebuilt. But where are the building blocks with which the cell rebuilds itself? These have to be supplied through the cell walls in the form of necessary organic molecules, particularly amino acids and sugar molecules,

which can be used to rebuild the architecture of the molecule, and
of course, in the beginning of any organism these molecules build
up, piece by piece, to form the organism as we see it. And it is
remarkable at this basic molecular level how alike these molecules
are, regardless of the life form in question.

To quote from Isaac Asimov's (1962) *The Wellsprings of Life*
(page 151):

> Potato starch, olive oil, and beef protein are eaten by man and out of
> them are produced human glycogen, human fat, human protein. What
> is the mysterious alchemy that brings about the conversion? Nothing more
> than this: the process of digestion breaks down the foreign food sub-
> stances to the building blocks that man holds in common with all crea-
> tures. It is the building blocks that are absorbed, the simple sugars, the
> fatty acids, and so on; and it is the building blocks that are then put back
> together again in a fashion that suits our own requirements.
> Chemically, all life is one.

This, then, is the situation with regard to one of the major assignments of every living creature—survival, the maintenance of its molecular structure.

The raccoon cannot assimilate a whole crayfish or a whole pellet.
The final encounter between the raccoon and this part of the environment, the crayfish or the pellet, must be molecular in nature.
However, it is also true that the whole raccoon cannot "do business"
or interact in terms of molecules. Both the parts of the raccoon and
the parts of the environment must be reduced to ever smaller and
smaller parts of systems until the final impingement of molecule
upon molecule is reached.

The fact of the molecular encounter can also be seen with regard
to the organism's second assignment of existence—reproduction. Because genes are molecules and the male and female genes must
unite to form a new organism, the end point of sexual reproduction
is the combination of molecular structures after the egg and sperm
come together. All the preactivities of the mating process—searching
out the potential mate, courting, and copulation—result finally in
this molecular encounter.

The molecular encounter can also be seen in pursuit and escape
(or rather, failure to escape). If the raccoon does not escape the dog,
after a rather considerable and bloody battle (and the process of

ingestion, digestion, and assimilation going on inside the dog), the raccoon's molecules may be recombined into dog molecules.

One can see that the psychologist and the behavioral scientist in general have confined their efforts to explaining this system in terms of getting the food into the mouth, getting the two animals to copulate, getting one animal to escape from the impinging danger, and so on. However, we feel that in order to see the real nature of the process, one must look at the whole transformation down to the molecule-to-molecule match; otherwise we are looking at so short a piece of the movie that we cannot possibly understand the plot.

The failure to integrate the whole sequence of events that take place between the organism and the environment has arisen because the academic world has been splintered into separate disciplines, each with its own level of discourse and explanation. As soon as the raccoon swallows the pellet, the psychologist forgets the whole episode and starts over with the sequence of behaviors that lead to a new pellet, leaving the next part of the process to the physiologist, who in turn may leave the end result to the biochemist down the hall. Nobody speaks for the raccoon.

We must not forget that the organism evolved and was carrying on commerce with the environment for millions of years before academic departments were devised. It seems increasingly evident that the most fruitful view will be to disregard these artificial compartmentalizations and deal with the full process from beginning to end, without honoring conventional divisions of subject matter. Indeed this departure is coming to be honored by many scientists in various fields who seek the unity of science, and is represented most promisingly quite recently by the "system thinkers"—generalists who attempt by conceptualizing a system (organismic, social, machine, or what have you) in its most generalized form to describe it and relate its behavior to other systems (Young, 1964).

Why this departure from the conventional viewpoint and why the inclusion of what appears to be material from other disciplines are necessary will become clearer when we get further along in explaining the behavior of animals. The "new look" in understanding behavior implies a unity that cuts across academic disciplinary boundaries and ignores the manner in which the subject matter is divided into academic departments and discussed at different levels.

We hope to show why in order to understand behavior it is necessary to consider the entire process of the encounter between the raccoon and the crayfish or the pellet, between the organism and the environment.

As far as the internal economy of the raccoon is concerned, and more important, as far as the fulfillment of his basic assignments of existence are concerned—namely, to survive and reproduce—the process is just beginning when he swallows the food. It is still necessary to consider the organismic system at the chemical molecular level. So, let us follow up the process.

Let us take the situation from the point of view of the vertebrate cell, remembering that the cell in turn is an organized molecular structure. The cell has no "knowledge," one would assume, of the vast expanse of the external world. All the cell "knows" is "I need something." It is ready to accept microportions of the environment that surround it and to adapt these to its uses. In other words, the cell requires certain substances for its regeneration. Because the ordinary vertebrate cell's major contact with the outside world is through the bloodstream, it can obtain what it needs only if in the bloodstream or other fluids of the organism there exist the necessary chemical molecular substances. Aside from unusual circumstances, such as intravenous feeding, these substances can get into the bloodstream only if they have been picked up out of the intestines by the papillae, the tiny "fingers" on the intestinal lining through which nutrients are absorbed. They can get into the intestines only if they have come down from the stomach (or gizzard, in the case of birds) and have been properly processed by the digestive juices. They can get into the stomach only if their precursors came in through the mouth and were churned up and worked upon perhaps first by the teeth and by the saliva, or otherwise processed. These precursors— food—can get into the mouth only if the gross total organism impinges upon, or is impinged upon by, suitable sources of this so-called food.

Now let us take the process back the other way and see what happens. Here we have a hungry animal, hunting in the forest for food. The fact that he is "hungry" means that he has been put on the forest path by an "upward" and "outward" coursing stream of activation—from the cells, which activated "messengers" in the bloodstream, from the bloodstream to the nervous system, where first the internal organs were activated (they start to churn and prepare the way for food)—this activation in turn wakes the animal up or activates his skeletal muscles so that he leaves his nest or den and goes hunting.

In this hunting process, he often uses a complex visual apparatus, a sense of smell, perhaps tactual senses, legs, paws, numerous skeletal muscles, many complex behavior sequences—walking, climbing, sniffing, scooping, and so on, and of course, all the nervous system channels, connections, and controls that go with all these parts and processes. Now the animal sees (or smells, perhaps, or both) some food—the environment impinges upon him, and he pounces and grabs, thereby impinging on the environment. He picks up the food and puts it into his mouth. Next he chews and swallows. Some digestive juice action has already started breaking down the food in the mouth, but when it reaches the stomach, more such action takes place. The stomach churns and pumps, causing further breakdown of the substances, getting it closer and closer to the point where the animal's cells can use it. The pumping action (known as peristalsis) continues on through the intestines, and now fully processed molecules are picked up through the papillae and enter the bloodstream, where the coursing of the blood, pumped by the heart action, carries the molecules to the cells; then they pass into the cell and are ultimately transformed into parts of the animal itself.

A closer look at these various processes will reveal a fact which we can simply state here but which will be further developed later on; namely, that the processes and bodily parts used in these various stages of satisfying the "cell hunger" differ in certain important and regular ways, and one of the most important is the evolutionary *age* of the parts and processes, the points in historical time at which these parts and processes began to appear in ancient species. The behaviors and the parts and processes that the raccoon used early in the hunting sequence are fairly recent developments in evolutionary time. Ancient, primitive animals did not have such fancy equipment. Similarly, the mouth parts, teeth, musculature of the swallowing apparatus, and so on, developed more recently in the historical development of animals than did the stomach, intestines, heart, blood vessels, and their types of action. The stomach, intestines, heart, blood vessels, and their processes in turn are newer in evolutionary history than the method by which the cell takes in the substances and transforms them into its own type of substance. From the foregoing two main points emerge:

1. Behavior sequences (at least those related to what the psychologist calls the primary drives, such as hunger) are basically internally activated; the activation goes from the "inside" to the "outside," from the old to the new. The old parts and processes are activated first, followed by successively newer ones, but—

2. In the process of satisfying a drive, such as hunger, the animal reels off sequences in the *opposite* direction—he normally and naturally regresses—that is, he starts with historically newer and more complicated processes and goes "down the ladder" to successively older and simpler processes.

We will see later that a somewhat different state of affairs exists with regard to behavior sequences having to do with flight and aggression, which are more externally "triggered" (Scott, 1965).

It is our belief, from experience with vast numbers of animals of numerous species, that these points are fundamental to an understanding of behavior. Behavior in general cannot be understood except in the framework of evolution. It may seem odd that a phenomenon cannot be understood on the face of it, so to speak, simply by observation of the phenomenon itself. However, we have found that you cannot understand the behavior of the animal in the laboratory unless you understand his behavior in the wild. And you cannot understand his behavior in the wild without understanding evolution. Indeed, you cannot even answer the questions "What is behavior?" "What is an animal?" or "What is the animal doing?" without an understanding of evolution. The trouble is that the animal does not come into the laboratory as a *tabula rasa*, a blank slate. He has certain parts, physiological processes, and built-in behavior patterns, all of which are the result of his evolutionary history, which exquisitely fit him to live in a particular portion of the environment (his ecological niche). (Of course the animal also has a personal history of which the experimenter may or may not have a detailed record.)

It also becomes increasingly evident that a true appreciation of mankind cannot be reached without an understanding of evolution and a wide acquaintance with a variety of other species. In order to understand what a remarkable animal man is, it is necessary to see him in comparison with the other species with whom he shares the world, and to see him in his full evolutionary perspective. To paraphrase Pascal, the great French philosopher of the seventeenth century, one should not tell man he is an animal without telling him what a wonderful animal he is. And to paraphrase the English poet Pope, the proper study of mankind is all animals.

The raccoon and the dog and man are, like all animals, the products of millions of years of evolution. The only reason that the raccoon is here in his present form is that he has been selected out from all the variants and failures of his kind and of his predecessors for his ability to survive and to reproduce. The dog similarly is here because over millions of years creatures who gradually came to look and act like this dog survived and reproduced. They survived because they were built like this dog and because they behaved as did this dog. (Of course, it is true that the dog's story is at least partly altered by man's intervention—the selection of certain types of dogs over others, to help man or to suit his whims.)

This, then, is the "business of living" in which the animal engages at all times—to preserve its own bodily integrity and to reproduce its kind. This means that, at least in the higher organisms, three or four categories or divisions of the organismic function and structure can be depicted. First, the animal has to find food in order to replenish the chemical molecules in the cells in its body, which are continuously disintegrating. Also, it has to build new cells in order to maintain its integrity as a system. Secondly, it has to avoid noxious and lethal injury; in other words, it has to eat but not be eaten. And thirdly, it has to reproduce its kind—in the higher animals, this means mating, the production of progeny, and in the more advanced species, the rearing of the young. In short, the raccoon and the dog and man are here representing evolutionary survival because their ancestors have succeeded better than some earlier variants along the line in living up to these three great assignments that evolution requires of its successful organisms.

In the process of achieving these big assignments, different species have evolved in a vast variety of directions. No animal can be said to "do business" with the environment as a whole. He is in direct contact and interacts with only a fraction of the total environment; this fraction constitutes his "ecological niche." Species in their various directions of evolution have come to occupy a tremendous range of these niches and have developed specialized structures and functions, specialized ways of doing business with certain segments of their environment. In other words, all animals are to a certain extent specialists, and some are very specialized indeed. Each animal's physical make-up, his morphology, and just as certainly and equally important, his behavior patterns have been specialized by countless generations of natural selection to fit the particular niche he occupies. The horse thus has hard hooves, long legs, and powerful leg muscles admirably suited for pounding across the plains; behaviorally he can run like the wind; visually he can detect minute movements and thus can spot the first approaches of a predator. All these adaptations enable the horse to survive on the flat grasslands, his ecological niche. Similarly, the perching birds have toes adapted to the small tree branches, keen vision for an aerial and arboreal life, and behaviorally the tendency to take off and fly swiftly and abruptly at the slightest threat from a predator.

In order, then, to understand what is going on, it may be well to take a closer look at the story of evolution.

THE THEORY OF EVOLUTION

Evolution is now considered not to be merely a theory. It might be better described as an inescapable inference on the basis of the evidence. However, the evidence, although overwhelming, is necessarily circumstantial, and some parts are stronger than others.

In brief, the theory of organic evolution says that plants and animals have changed by steps, some small, some large, through generation after generation and are still changing today and that these stepwise changes have been passed by heredity from one generation to the next. If they are changes that help the organism survive and reproduce, more organisms showing these changes will result than if the changes are lethal or disadvantageous. In other words, the changes and the organisms exhibiting them are acted upon by natural selection from the environment—those that are selected for survival and reproduction persist; those that are not perish. Because these changes have been going on for hundreds of millions of years, all things now living on the earth are thus the greatly altered descendants of ancient forms.

There are various kinds of evidence for evolution, which we will mention briefly and need not discuss in detail. First, we can see it before our eyes—the spontaneous production of new breeds and species in the wild, the production of new breeds of domestic plants, such as the Concord grape, and animals, such as the tumbler pigeon, by human breeders. (In fact, it was the sight of these products of man's artificial selection that led Darwin to his great thought that nature's version of this same process led to the evolution of new species in the wild—natural selection instead of artificial.)

Secondly, one of the major lines of evidence is the fossil record, showing orderly change from simple forms in the ancient rocks to more complicated and specialized forms as time goes on. One of the best such records depicts the evolution of the horse, whose ancestors 70 million years ago were like all the other mammals—small and generalized. Countless fossil descendants show the gradual changes that fit the modern horse for life on the grassy plains. Not all fossil records are this good—there are many gaps and mysteries, but the general plan is inescapable.

Thirdly, embryology shows the developing embryo of a complex modern organism recapitulating or repeating in a rough way many of the stages that are typical of simpler forms—for example, in the development of the dog embryo the heart will pass through various stages like those of the fish, the amphibian, and the reptile until it finally assumes the four-chambered mammalian form. This very basic concept is known as the *biogenetic law*. It can be stated as "ontogeny recapitulates phylogeny," meaning that the individual in his development retraces the development of the race. Here again, there are gaps and "short circuits" in the process, but the general trend is unmistakable.

Comparative anatomy and physiology offer a fourth class of evidence. Fossil fin bones in ancient fish, amphibian limbs, horse's legs and hooves, bat's wings, dolphin's flippers, and human arms and hands can all be seen as related structures. For example, in the bat's wing or the dissection of a dolphin's flipper, you can see all the basic five digits of the general primitive vertebrate member, just as you can in your own sets of five toes and five fingers. Also in the dolphin, who apparently descended from an ancestor of the modern ungulates—cows, goats, sheep, and so on—we can see the vertebrate hip bones represented only by two small vestigial bones (Slijper, 1962). Similarly, blood chemistry can also show links between groups—for example, man resembles the apes, particularly the chimpanzee, in many blood groups and various tests run on the blood—hemoglobin, serum albumin, and so forth (Coon, 1962)—and serum agglutination tests have linked the cetaceans with the ungulates (Boyden and Gemeroy, 1950).

Finally, geographical evidence is sometimes useful, especially in the development of speciation on isolated islands or other cutoff areas. Thus, where mating between populations is cut off by water, high mountain ranges, or other severe physical barriers, species tend to develop in their own peculiar ways, with a resulting fauna peculiar to that isolated region. One of the most famous examples of this is the fauna of the Galapagos Islands, off the coast of South America, where Darwin was startled by the uniqueness of the animal species—turtles, birds, lizards—native and unique to these islands but similar to those on the nearby shores of the American continent (Darwin, 1859).

THE EVOLUTIONARY STORY

What, then, does the evidence indicate about the evolutionary story? For general documentation of this and the preceding section you may refer to such recent biology texts as Moment (1958), the *Life* Nature Library volume (Moore, 1960), *Man, Time and Fossils* (Moore, 1963), or other standard works.

The evolution of life on earth cannot really be separated from the evolution of the planet itself. Although the time when life first appeared on the planet cannot be pinpointed, the geological record indicates vast eons prior to the origins of life, during which the earth itself was forming and evolving. In addition to the gross geological upheavals that produced the mountains, the valleys, and the seas, changes in fine structures also, of course, took place—atoms had formed into molecules and molecules into chemical compounds. Particularly, the sea waters were developing into a primordial "soup" of complex organic and inorganic substances which were to prove to be suitable combinations for the appearance of what were to become the first living forms.

Although the biologist has largely concerned himself with *organic* evolution, there has been a growing body of knowledge deriving from the work of the biochemists concerning the evolution of the nonliving precursors of living forms. Just as there are no reasons to assume there have been big jumps or gaps in the organic evolutionary pattern, there is no reason to assume a hiatus between life and nonlife. Although the evolution of life from nonliving chemical compounds may sound preposterous, it is more preposterous to suppose that even the simplest one-celled animal, the primitive precursor, say, of the amoeba, came full-blown from nowhere. There must have been transitional simpler forms prior to the simplest one-celled animals, and the question of how these may have arisen has been the subject of lively inquiry in biochemistry in recent years.

The work of Haldane, Oparin, Urey, Fox, Melvin Calvin, and others (Oparin, 1957), indicates that given the right molecular configurations under the right combination, life will arise spontaneously. Although the story of the evolution of life itself is not quite on as firm ground as organic evolution, something very much like the following must have happened.

The generally held view now is that life arose from the primordial ocean, which contained a variety of complex substances in dilution. The energy for the first syntheses of lifelike molecular structures came perhaps from ultraviolet radiation or lightning. From here on natural selection favored the self-duplicating, molecular configuration that was autocatalytic and thus able to create reactions by means of one of its own products. These configurations, then, were able to obtain needed energy by decomposing and resynthesizing some of the complex molecules already formed, and life was off and flying, so to speak.

No fossil record exists from these far-off times, although there are deposits that may have been made by certain bacterialike living things. The tiny evolving molecules and single-celled organisms belonged to the simplest large biological categories—the protozoans or single-celled animals, such as the amoeba and paramecium—and the Protophyta or single-celled plants—bacteria, simple algae, and so on. These, as well as the soft-tissued, gelatinous ancestors of the metazoans, or multicelled animals, left no bony or crusty parts to be deposited in the ancient ocean beds or the rocks of these times (sometimes called pre-Cambrian). A few uncertain fossils, such as body imprints and the like, appear in rocks that may be 1,000 million years old, and we do know that evolution was proceeding during these vast stretches of time, because dating from the early times of what is called the Paleozoic era, about 550 million years ago, fossils are found of small, generalized representatives of all the major nonvertebrate phyla—ancestors of the porifera or sponges, the coelenterates (sea anemones, jellyfish, and hydras), molluscs, flatworms, roundworms, annelids (earthworms), and arthropods (insects, crustaceans, and the like). Some of these ancient types survive today virtually unchanged (jellyfish, for example).

From here on the pattern of evolution is much clearer. It proceeded steadily from simple to the more complex. Species changed gradually, developing special features, surviving, dying out as the environment changed, or as other features that they developed made them less able to survive and reproduce. The earlier forms tend to be more generalized and simpler. Gradually specializations develop, and with them, complexity.

The environment to which the evolving species were able to adapt was also becoming more complex. In the case of the preliving forms, bare molecular structures, the process of synthesizing more of themselves consisted simply of attaching themselves directly to the proper chemical compounds, which they found all around them. Once the cell was encapsulated, or enclosed in a cell wall, it was necessary for the cell in some fashion to admit the chemical compounds necessary for further synthesis of the cell's own compounds. But still these simple primitive creatures floated around with suitable edible materials all around them and had only to "open up" or flow around particles and admit them.

Then as multicelled animals began to evolve, some cells began to specialize—some in breaking down and resynthesizing other compounds (forerunners of digestive cells), while others began to specialize in functions that had to do with the organism's getting around in the environment—for example, forerunners of modern muscle cells developed to specialize in moving the animal to a more favorable spot; sensory cells developed that could detect favored particles and also warn the animal of danger. Still, as long as these primitive animals stayed in rich areas of the mother sea, they had largely simply to pump the soup in and out and take what they wanted from it. Many simple animals still function in this fashion— for example, the sponges and the lugworm. But as more and more animals occupied this simple niche, the nutritive elements available in such a milieu began to become more scarce, and animals began to develop new structures and habits to make contact with those parts of the environment that they needed. So the whole trend of evolution from these ancient, easy times has been to enable successively more complicated species to live in more and more complicated and difficult environments.

For example, probably about 450 to 400 million years ago (although the time tables are uncertain and there is some disagreement among scholars), fresh water and probably land plants appeared, both events requiring considerable adaptations on the parts of the plants to live in the more hostile realms of the land. Also about this time the first vertebrates appear—the primitive jawless fishes probably derived from primitive marine chordates, the larger overall group to which the vertebrates belong. (Most likely the ancestor was a larval or infant form of a tunicate—more about this later.) And the simpler phyla also were developing more and more specializations which enabled them to react to the environment.

Then about 365 million years ago, the sharklike fishes began to appear, and then rather suddenly about 350 million years ago bony fishes began to appear along with the first primitive generalized amphibians. These, as well as some arthropods, began to invade the land. After another vast stretch of time, the first small reptiles appeared, descended apparently from an early generalized amphibian form, and some ambitious specializing creatures—the flying insects—first took to the air, again adding another environment to which living things could adapt.

Finally, about 200 million years ago began the age of the great reptiles, and as these creatures specialized and grew progressively larger, the first primitive mammals began to evolve from a form like the much earlier so-called dog-toothed lizard, and the birds took off from reptilian stock in a direction of their own.

Some parts of mammalian evolution are better recorded than others (and again the dividing lines of temporal periods are blurred over millions or hundreds of thousands of years), but it is clear that from small, generalized, vaguely rodentlike or shrewlike ancestral stock a vast explosive radiation and evolution of various mammalian types took place beginning roughly about 100 million years ago, culminating perhaps about 1 million to 700,000 years ago in what man considers the apex of evolution, *Homo sapiens*.

Vertebrate Evolution

Behavior studies are not confined to vertebrate species, and indeed many valuable observations and experiments have been made on protozoa, insects (see reading [1]), flatworms, earthworms, and so on. With these lowly species some pioneering work of great theoretical significance was done in the late nineteenth and the early twentieth century by such men as Loeb, Verworn, Lubbock, and Jennings (Warden, Jenkins, and Warner, 1935). However, the bulk of behavior studies and the major interest of the behavioral sciences have been concerned with the vertebrates. Therefore, at this point it might be well to go back a bit and consider in more detail the evolution of this group of animals.

There is strong evidence that modern vertebrates trace their ancestry to a simple animal rather like the larvae of certain modern tunicates (Romer, 1958). The tunicate is one of the chordate phylum but has, instead of bony vertebrae down his back, simply a gristly rod, or notochord. The tunicate in the adult form is mainly a sessile filter-feeder, meaning that it simply sits rooted in one spot and filters the water in and out, taking its nutrients from the water. However, as an infant, the tunicate can move around; in fact, it looks quite unlike its adult self and more like a small, simple fish, and even more like the lancelet, *Amphioxus*—a fishlike in-between animal—somewhere between a primitive chordate and a true vertebrate. It is an ancient form of this larva that seems to be ancestral to the vertebrates—a larva that one day reached sexual maturity without otherwise growing up anatomically (a condition known as neoteny).

Now the larval form, having reached sexual maturity without assuming the adult form, no doubt found itself a "better deal." It could move around, locate food, escape enemies. From here on, gradually and step by tiny step, forms like these evolved into forms like the lancelet and finally into forms like primitive fish. In the pattern of this evolution, as traced by observation of living descendants of the primitive forms, and as read in the fossil record, we see increasing evidence of advancing sensory structures, nervous system, and locomotor powers. With these developments went adaptation to more and more complex environments, and steadily increasing dependence on and relation to environmental "stimuli." More and more the developing fishlike creatures moved around; more and more their sense organs improved, and thus they could tell where they were going and find food in waters poorer in nutrients.

Furthermore, another interesting thing happened to our primitive vertebrate; it still had the visceral equipment of the old adult form —designed to pump the sea in and out and release reproductive cells into the water when they were mature—but it had the motor and sensory equipment of the infant form—simple visual and equilibrium organs and a simple brain, which in the original form probably guided the larva's movements to a suitable spot for the adult to settle down. Thus, in a sense, this animal was two animals in the same skin.

Two main points emerge from this history of the vertebrates. One, that the ability to react to outside, distant stimulation is essentially an "improvement patent" (a variation on the basic system which improves but does not alter the primary functioning) on the primitive, simple, internally determined behavior that goes on virtually willy-nilly, unrelated by sensory control to what is happening in the external world. Although it is true that massive external changes (temperature, for example) could alter the speed or even occurrence of behavior, the primitive animal in an environment favorable to it could carry on its basic life functions almost regardless of whether the time and place were right. More highly evolved animals depend on cues from the environment to determine the time and place of their behavioral and functional efforts. So it appears that the basic beginnings of any sequence of behavior are internally, primitively determined by the internal arousal of the older systems, whereas the newer portions—locomotion and bodily muscular and sensory reactions of all sorts—have evolved and take place when the old primitive sequences cannot go on in their old way, simply by pumping in and out. The capacity for stimulus acceptance thus tells the animal, "Don't pump now, there's nothing there to eat" or "You can start now. We are close to food." These new processes and improvements thus serve the older parts and processes and make possible their survival in the world which is now less favorable for the survival of the simple primitive animal.

The second point concerns neoteny, which if this story of vertebrate evolution is correct, is "built into" the vertebrates from their earliest ancestry. Although biologists differ in their interpretation of neoteny as a concept, it has a sound status applied in its narrow sense, and used broadly is a rich and useful tool in understanding the behavior of man and many of his fellow vertebrates. All that this principle of neoteny means in a most generalized form is that animals may be fully adult in many respects, including sexual reproduction, but remain infantile in many others. The dictionary definition refers to it as "the condition of having the period of immaturity indefinitely prolonged." If the vertebrates evolved in the first place by achieving sexual maturity before full anatomical maturity, then we might well suppose that this tendency might reappear in subsequent vertebrate species. Indeed, we do see it often in many present-day vertebrate species, and there is good evidence that it has operated in past evolutions—in the evolution of man, for example, from an apelike predecessor (Coon, 1962).

One might say that the whole mammalian class is in some way neotenized, chiefly in the prolonged extension of the dependency of the young. More specific examples may be seen in playfulness of adult animals like raccoons, monkeys, and dolphins. Many if not all of man's domestic animals are quite neotenized; the average domestic dog is an extremely infantile creature compared with a wolf or a fox; he whines, cries, fawns, and plays in a puppyish fashion, and many of his old instinctive patterns do not fully mature —some highly selected species make indifferent parents; high-bred dogs may soil their beds. The domestic cat also seems immature or neotenized compared with the wild felines. It cries and rubs up against human legs for food as the kitten does with the mother cat. Again, much of the wild feline's desperate ferocity is attenuated.

Many of man's physical and behavioral properties afford the best examples. Physically, the hairless skin (and general hair distribution) is like that of the fetal chimpanzee. The large head and the angle at which it joins the neck also resemble those of the fetal apes. Behaviorally man has almost no mature instinctive patterns remaining—the civilized mother, without instruction, is almost unable to care for her baby. Man remains dependent on parents for years past sexual maturity, and indeed, never gives up his emotional dependence on some kind of a "father figure"—the cultural heroes, gods, doctors, priests, and national leaders.

THE EVOLUTION OF THE NERVOUS SYSTEM

Another important state of affairs, which is true of other phyla but can be seen most clearly in the vertebrate story, concerns the steady evolution of the nervous system. Starting with a simple collection of primitive ganglia at the forward end of the spinal cord, the vertebrate brain has developed mainly in the direction of proliferations of nerve cells surrounding and overlying the more primitive structures. These primal ancient collections of cells—ganglia, centers, such structures as the thalamus, the medulla oblongata—were, in the ancestral vertebrates and still are in higher vertebrates, concerned with the basic life functions—maintenance of circulation, breathing, digestion, and so on. As the newer forms evolved and increased the size and complexity of their brains, the newer areas became increasingly concerned with evolutionarily newer kinds of behavior and the innervation of new structures—and increasingly with maintaining contact with the environment and reacting to more and more complex and unfriendly environments. The growth in size and complexity of the nervous system made it ever more capable of processing more data and innervating more complex structures. Along with this development came fancier receptors—complex eyes and ears—and sensitive and skillful hands and fingers, although it might sometimes be difficult to pinpoint temporally which was the cart and which the horse in these evolutionary sequences.

At any rate, examining a progressive series of vertebrate brains, from fish to amphibian to reptile to mammal, and through the mammalian series up to man, we see a gradual bulging of newer nervous tissues, gray matter, or cerebral cortex and the increasing bulge of the cerebellum, which concerns itself with motor coordination and equilibrium (as might be expected, this is prominent in the birds). These evolutionarily newer overlays are increasingly concerned with relation to and adaptation to the environment and with the control and use of newer evolutionary structures and functions, and again, the evolutionarily new processes function "in the service of" the old.

THE DIFFERENTIAL AGE OF PARTS AND PROCESSES

Now as you may have detected from all this, it is evident that in any modern organism, some of his structures and processes are evolutionarily older than others. The basic mammalian gut evolved long ago and has changed less with subsequent evolution than, say, the mammalian foot or hand. (Incidentally, it is interesting to note that bilateral symmetry is not characteristic of the gut, although most other portions of a vertebrate are bilaterally symmetrical— one side being a virtual mirror image of the other.) Similarly, the nervous structures that control the heart beat and the digestive processes are evolutionarily more ancient than those controlling speech; the midbrain is older than the cerebral cortex; and these portions of the nervous system too have changed less from amphibian to man, say, than has the outer layer of the cortex.

Consequently, we can order the organism's parts and processes and functions into a rough hierarchy according to evolutionary age, from newer to older, or neoteric to primal. This hierarchy refers, of course, not only to physical structures but also to behavior patterns, which are the natural functions of the structures. Also the different parts and processes seem to have different dynamic properties according to their evolutionary age. The behavior of playing the piano can be expected to have different properties than eating, swallowing, the action of the intestines, and the assimilation of molecules. It is more variable, it is more related to the environment, and its internal sequences are far more interchangeable.

SUMMARY: THE PATTERN OF VERTEBRATE LIFE

We are now in a fairly good position to see the basic pattern or paradigm of animal, or more particularly, vertebrate life. A typical vertebrate, such as the raccoon, and indeed, a typical representative of any highly evolved species, finds itself in a vastly more complicated environment than did its remote aquatic ancestors in the primordial sea. It cannot simply open up and take in the nutritive parts of the environment but must wait until the signs are right.

As we have seen, in order for the raccoon to do business in the modern forest, there must be a mutual regression process between the organism and his environment. This means that the organism and the environment must be worked back mutually and simultaneously to the point where a molecule-to-molecule match can take place in order for the raccoon ultimately to fit itself to its environment—the ingested protein must become raccoon protein, the genes must match.

With this necessity in mind, we might take a look at how the activation of the nervous system may work to bring about the necessary processes in a complex animal. The following might be considered a hypothesis of nervous action, a hypothetical brain model. There are many models of the action of the brain, but none really is successful in a descriptive sense. Most have been designed in the stimulus–response paradigm, where the external inputs to sense organs are treated as the initiating events. The following is a model or paradigm of brain action which we have found useful in describing what the animal is doing.

The sequence of events that determines what we actually see in the gross bodily movement in the organism begins when the internal and evolutionarily very ancient systems begin to need replenishment; this beginning of disintegration "fires up" the very old message-carrying channels of the organism first. The cell needs molecules; the "message" sent by the cell gives rise to activation in the nervous system, with the older sections being activated first. These, however, are blocked off, prevented from carrying through their activities by the evolutionarily newer parts of the nervous system, which have, as we have noted, steadily evolved in the direction of relating the organism's basic activities to the environment. The internal behavior of the organism thus cannot take place; indeed, it would be useless for it to do so. The food is not there to be taken in. The organism as a whole must await the impingement of suitable portions of the now nonhomogeneously distributed environment in order to make a successful encounter. However, these old, internal processes or channels are "hot," and in turn they pass the message on to the successively newer parts and processes of the nervous system, thus bringing the newer parts of the organism into action to do business in this particular environment. This we call "backward activation." (Please keep in mind we are speaking here of such primary and basic activation processes as hunger and sex, not of such sequences as flight and aggression—Scott, 1965.)

Thus, the raccoon has been put into action from the inside out, so to speak; his evolutionarily ancient systems are activated and coursing outward to put into action the evolutionarily newer ones. He goes hunting.

He finds a crayfish and eats it. Now his digestive juices must process the crayfish and break down the crayfish protein to the point where the molecules in the cells of the raccoon's body can assimilate it. As this regressive process goes on, from the beginning of the cycle to its end point at the molecular match, the raccoon uses first evolutionarily new (for example, learned reactions to visual cues in the forest), then progressively older parts and processes of his body (pouncing, chewing, digesting, assimilating).

When we look at the segment of activity with which the psychologist has principally concerned himself, we are looking merely at the first externally obvious steps of the process by which the organism reaches the molecular match. However, in order to understand any segment of the process, we must see the whole regressive process itself, in its entirety, and as a fundamental pattern.

We can see from all this that we must be interested not only in the sequences of the overt muscular contractions with which the psychologist has been primarily and customarily concerned, but also in the processes of the organism as a whole. Everything that goes on must be taken into account—the overt muscular contractions, the salivation, the churning and grinding of the stomach, the secretion of the digestive juices, the absorption through the intestinal wall, and the ultimate molecular synthesis inside the cell. The action of the stomach's hydrochloric acid on the food swallowed is a part of the behavior of the animal, just as much as hunting, pouncing, chewing, and swallowing. It is an essential link in the chain, and at no point can we break off the flow of causative events. The whole sequence makes up the grand paradigm of survival.

To sum up: there are two fundamental points in this development of the organism's evolutionary history and the nature of his molecular encounter with the environment: first, that *behavior is basically activated internally*, from the "inside out," and second, that *regression is a natural and inevitable part of everyday, ongoing behavior;* in everyday business with the environment, the organism regularly regresses in his behavioral processes down to more and more primitive processes.

CYCLICAL SEQUENCES OF BEHAVIOR

The sequential nature of behavior is its foremost and definitive property. Sequences at the overt level of behavior (behavior we can see as opposed to that which goes on inside the animal) are patterns of muscular contractions, and ultimately involve processes within the molecules of each muscle cell. At any moment there are numerous muscles in various states of contraction. In fact, there are so many that only by means of a very elaborate control system can an animal do anything at all. Simply to walk or even to move a limb requires a remarkable coordination of various muscular contractions.

Consider a newly hatched baby chick, with its collection of "uneducated," unused muscle cells. The chick, of course, has many more than 100 muscle cells, indeed, more than 100 bundles of cells known as muscles. But even if there were only 100, it might be an interesting arithmetical exercise to calculate the probability that the proper sequence of contractions would occur so that the chick would get up and walk. This, of course, is what the chick does without hesitation and without elaborate learning.

It is obvious that certain sequences of behavior are built-in, innate, or instinctive. Like the animal's physical structure, these sequences have evolved in such a fashion as to result in the survival of the animal in the environmental niche in which he finds himself. They come already "wired in" to the elaborate control system, which in the vertebrate and other advanced organisms is the central nervous system.

Thus, we see that the movable parts of the organism work in sequences and that they can do so without depending on environmental inputs, being basically dependent on internal activation for their initiation. Furthermore, these sequences are cyclical in character, as are all organismic processes. The chick puts one foot forward, then the other; he has taken a step. Then the first leg recycles, and then the second one. He is now walking. This is a cycle within a cycle, and there are many such in organismic processes—gross ones stretched out in time, molecular ones occurring in minutes or seconds. Larger cycles in the chick's life might be described as "following his mother"—she walks away, he follows until he catches up—she walks away again, and so on—or as "searching for food." To accomplish each larger cycle, the chick must go through the smaller cycle of walking many times; to follow his mother or reach the food pan, his little legs must cycle and recycle many times.

This, then, is the fundamental behavioral process at the conventional psychologist's level—without the built-in, recycling sequence, the psychologist could do nothing. Connected sequences must be there before the psychologist can do anything with the animal. As the operant psychologist [3] would say, the "operant must exist at some strength before it can be reinforced." All learning, all behavior study is achieved by utilizing at first already existing cyclical sequences.

RELATIVE CONNECTABILITY

One extremely important point about these built-in sequences of behavior is that they come in all degrees of fixity or levels of determination. Some are from the very beginning tightly "wired in" and virtually unaffected by anything that later happens to the animal.

Often these are the older, more conservative features relating to the basic survival of the animal: nerve connections insuring that the heart will beat, that the animal will breathe—many of the fundamental locomotor patterns. These are often quite rigid and stereotyped for the species or even for the higher group to which the species belongs. Some are virtually completely "wired" and need only a little experience with the environment to polish them up, such as the sequences concerned with flying in the perching birds, for example. The little bird leaves the nest with the basic equipment, both muscular and nervous, for flying. The sequences are there, and will occur, and they are typical of their species—the first flight sequences of the baby bluebird are different in pattern from those of the sparrow. We have all seen the tentative, hesitant, short "practice" flights of the fledglings, fluttering from limb to limb and from limb to ground and back as they perfect these sequences into the coordinated smooth pattern of the adult bird.

To a certain extent, the degree to which these muscular patterns that constitute the repertoire of the organism are fixed, determinate, and relatively unchangeable is a function of the phylogenetic level to which the animal belongs. It is also a function of whether the animal is a narrow-niche or a broad-niche animal—that is, does the animal occupy a very restricted part of the environment: does he make his living from only a small segment of it, or does he range widely in his niche and feed freely? Thus, the patterned sequences of a fish are more fixed and show less change with environmental experience than those of a raccoon. Similarly, relatively more fixed behavior sequences are seen in the rabbit, for example, than in the raccoon, because the former occupies a relatively invariable, narrow niche of the environment, whereas the latter is a wide-ranging, broad-niche animal. The rabbit lives only on the ground and eats only vegetable foods; the raccoon is at home on the ground, in the trees, and to some extent in the water, and is omnivorous—he will eat anything. The rabbit has relatively more invariable patterned sequences—he runs, hops, sniffs, digs, scratches, and pulls—and very little else. The raccoon does all of these and many more; he climbs, manipulates things with his paws, "plays," and so on.

Continuing with this analysis, we see that behavior sequences can come in all degrees of fixity, from virtually complete predetermination, so that every animal of a given species exhibits this behavior in just about this same form, to a great flexibility and alterability with learning. Man has virtually no complex sequences of built-in, "pre-wired" behaviors, except those connected with breathing, heart beat, digestion, a few isolated reflexes, and a few sequences concerned with locomotion, although even the last can be modified dramatically through learning. Similarly, the other higher mammals, the great generalizers, such as the apes and the dolphins, show relatively few fixed behavior sequences and many, many possible modifications and variations of muscular patterns with learning. However, even in these higher mammals some things are much easier to learn than others—fear of snakes in humans is apparently not innate but is certainly tremendously easy to condition. This ease of conditioning to certain stimuli may be the source of the almost universal symbols and fetishes noticed by Freudian psychologists—apparently it is easy for people to learn to attach sexual significance to snake symbols, to become abnormally fond of furry objects, and the like. Vocalizations in humans are easily learned and "shaped"; on the other hand, teaching a chimpanzee to open latches of all sorts is a simple task, but it is quite difficult to shape its vocalizations.

This continuum of "learnability" ends at the extreme of complete unlearnability. There are some things apparently that are completely unconnectable—for example, it is apparently impossible, or at least extremely difficult to the point of impossibility, to condition the alarm cry of the chicken to food reinforcement.

The ease of imprinting is an interesting example of ease of "learning." Imprinting is the process by which a baby bird or animal comes to identify its parent, or, in artificial cases, some other object or animal (Moltz, 1960). The duckling tends normally to follow its mother duck within a few hours after hatching; however, if for some reason the mother duck is not there, and the duckling sees instead a moving human being or a moving chicken, or even a mechanical toy, it will follow this object. After a few such experiences (sometimes only one), it learns to follow this moving object and this one alone. The process of learning is not only very rapid but in many cases is irreversible. We then say that the duckling has been imprinted to the human or the chicken or the toy and will never thereafter follow its mother duck.

Imprinting occurs more regularly and more rigidly in some species than in others and can be seen to a certain extent even in mammals. Mary's little lamb, for example, was imprinted to a human (such a lamb is known among sheepherding people as a "cosset").

Such imprinted animals make excellent experimental subjects because they are not afraid of people; we habitually imprint ducks for this purpose.

Imprinting thus is a case where the behavioral sequence or process is not quite hooked up or rigid when the baby animal comes into the world, but the "works" are all there for it to become so connected, and once the connection is made, in many species, it is fixed, rigid, and almost irreversible. Here is a sequence dependent on learning for one link only, and once the learning has taken place, there can be little or no unlearning.

The End of the Instinct–Learning Dichotomy

One of the oldest and most disputed problems in psychological history is the instinct–learning problem. Generally this problem takes the form of inquiring whether or not a given sequence of behavior in an animal is innate or learned, or perhaps whether most of the behavior patterns of a given animal are more influenced by learning or by heredity. The problem has been the cause of many emotional outbursts and the source of thousands of printed words. As we see it, it is really no problem at all.

In our view, the major point at issue is not instinct versus learning, not the learned versus the unlearned. The salient point is that organisms do in the course of their existence become organized to behave in certain ways: the major consideration is by no means whether the particular sequence under observation is primarily determined by genetics and embryology or whether it is more determined by the nature of the impinging environment; the major consideration is that the organism *does* organize itself, either as an embryo or after it enters the world at large. Behavior sequences, like the animal's physical equipment, do develop—they become hooked up, connected, either in embryology, by maturation, or by what is commonly called learning. There is an increasing indication that all connections of this sort depend ultimately on molecular changes in the nerve cells, and biochemically the connections formed genetically in the embryo or by maturation may not turn out to be very different from those formed by learning. The organizing or patterning of the behavior is thus the central issue.

Man in his thinking has tended to be trapped by the drama of the birth or hatching process of animals and birds, as if this were where the organism started. This ancient way of looking at nature goes back to a time in which man was completely ignorant of embryology. However, we know now, as a result of studies of evolution, physiology, and embryology, that there is no real breaking-off place, that the birth of a higher organism is a fairly insignificant event (Kuo, 1932), and that the organism comes equipped with a great many crystallized patterns of behavior and other processes.

It seems to be the case that, because of the historical development of behavior theory, and because of the predominant ways of looking at the behavior of animals, learning has been given a point of prominence that is totally out of keeping with the facts of nature. Much of the behavior of an organism, meaning everything that goes on within that organized system that we call an organism, is, for the most part, nonenvironmentally determined. Perhaps 99 percent of the life-serving processes of an organism consists of internal interaction between the different parts, processes, systems, and subsystems of that organism—cells, molecules, and so on.

If we study even the externally visible behavior of the incredible number of species in the animal world, of which about three-fourths are insects and perhaps another fifth are invertebrates other than insects, we can see that most organisms enter the world prepared to cope with it; even their behavior that is determined by or oriented to the environment is already preprogramed. Certain moths, for example, come equipped to respond only to a certain type of odor—that of the opposite sex of their own species. The lovebird comes ready, at maturity, to carry nest materials in a certain way, and the manner of carrying (whether by beak or under the wing) differs from one closely related species to another (Dilger, 1962).

Thus, learning is not one of nature's most prevalent ways of guaranteeing the preservation and reproduction of the individual or the species. Learning is an advanced "improvement patent," and to view animal behavior primarily within the framework of learning is to miss a great deal of nature's basic program or format.

In other words, even if we view the organism as a whole, and view the commerce between the organism and the environment over the whole spectrum of animal species, we can see that nature does not bet very heavily on the learning process. Her first bet is to build in certain fixed sequences that will equip the organism to fit itself to a very particular and very narrow piece of the environment. There are behaviors, sequences of events, muscular or otherwise, that will fire off in a particular sequence and in a particular sequence only, and they will do so in the presence of very clearly, already predetermined aspects of the environment. Thus the fighting behavior of the male robin will fire off in the presence of a very small and specialized piece of the environment, namely, the red patch on the breast of another male robin. The ethologists (see reading [4]) have shown that it is the red patch primarily, and not the male robin as a whole, that provides what they call the "releaser" mechanism; experiments with such objects as a ball of cotton bearing a red patch have shown the robin will fight such a synthetic rival.

One might say that the fitness to the environment is by and large determined genetically and embryologically. However, this viewpoint in no way casts learning in a pejorative or derogatory light. It seems to be equally clear that evolution has progressed toward ever more dependence on learning as the mechanism of fitness to a variable and complex environment in the later evolutionary species, of which man considers himself to be the crowning glory. In man the situation has become virtually scandalous, biologically speaking. Ancient as man's inner and basic processes may be, he knows very little when he hits the world; he is heavily dependent upon learning to equip him to get along in his environment. As we have already noted elsewhere, if we exclude the all-important physiological processes, man has, as innate behavioral equipment, only a few gross reflexes, such as the knee jerk and the eye wink, breathing, and some vague tendencies—possibly the female's love for babies and the male's propensity for picking fights with other males. Thus, apparently civilized man must learn to do virtually everything—how to woo a mate, even how to mate, how to care for a baby, how to hunt for food. We can say without any question that most of the higher forms of life would not survive unless their learning mechanisms were developed and working well.

PROPERTIES OF THE NATURAL REGRESSION PROCESS

We have seen that behavioral sequences, like the physical structures and physiological processes of the organism, can be ordered in a series, from old to new—from evolutionarily primitive to quite recent in time; similarly, that a typical behavior sequence of the type studied by psychologists begins with an activation of a primitive biological process that is blocked or interrupted because of the kind of environment in which the animal finds itself. The blocking mechanism is more than a simple physical restraint—it involves physiological and neurological blocks mediated by the newer parts of the nervous system, which have evolved to prevent the now inappropriate sequences from firing off blindly; and even more important, to enable the animal to "long-circuit" or get around the unfavorable conditions and make progress down the line toward solving his biological problems.

In the course of unreeling or performing this typical behavior sequence the animal uses "new" behaviors first, then progressively older and more primitive ones, until the final molecule-to-molecule match is achieved. One would suspect that the evolutionarily older behavior processes might have different properties than the more recently evolved ones, and this does indeed seem to be the case. In view of what has been said about the difference between learned and innate behaviors, one would also suspect that these property differences would apply equally to the learned sequences, and again this seems to be the case: the old and the new in learned sequences also tend to differ.

The following set of observations are not tightly checked experimentally. They might be regarded as experimental hypotheses, and indeed a very interesting experimental program can be developed to check them out. We can say, however, that these differences in properties from old to new check out in many field observations, and careful, critical field observation of the sort practiced by the ethologists and the scientifically trained naturalist has as good scientific standing as an experimental finding. So let us examine some of the differences as we have noted them:

1. The evolutionarily older, more primitive behavior processes are more dependent upon internal activation and interconnections and are less dependent upon and less connected to environmental impingements or stimuli than are the more recently evolved processes. The actions of the small intestine particularly go on virtually automatically and with little relation to the outside world, whereas brachiation (swinging from limb to limb, as practiced by some of the apes) requires keen coordination with the environmental impinge.

2. Stress (drive, emotion, strong needs) activates the sequences at the primal end of the regressive process more than those at the recent end. An example of this is seen in the state of hunger so widely used in psychological experimentation. The dog's stomach may begin to contract and his alimentary system in general may be partially activated (including some salivation), but psychic chewing movements (chewing when no food is in the mouth) are exceedingly rare, even though the animal is very hungry; also, dogs do not chase imaginary rabbits (very often) nor make bone-gnawing movements unless a bone is there.

3. Sequences at the primitive or primal end are more tightly tied together and are less interchangeable than those at the recent end. If you hold a dog's mouth shut and raise his head, the flow of saliva will eventually cause the dog to swallow, but you cannot get the dog to start a swallow in the middle of the sequence—the sequence must start at the beginning and continue to its end. However, if you look at a more recently evolved sort of sequence, such as certain types of hunting behavior, many segments may be freely interchanged: the dog may run, stop, sniff, turn his head from side to side, sniff again, run, turn his head, sniff, and so on. The subcycles are not tied tightly one to another in any particular order from one end of the hunting cycle to its conclusion.

4. As the regression process proceeds from newer to older sequences, the rate of action tends to build up. The newer sequences may start out rather slowly, but then as they reach the primal ones, they speed up. Rats run faster through the last parts of a maze. A hunting dog may start out coursing lackadaisically through the woods, but just let him hit a hot trail! A learned sequence with similar properties has caused sea lion trainers a great deal of trouble. A sea lion trained to play a tune on the horns (after which he receives a piece of fish) "smears" the last five or six notes into a very rapid slide.

5. The more primitive sequences are more readily connected to each other neurologically than the newer ones (but only in their normal sequences). Walking sequences in the chick (which are evolutionary extensions of fin movements in the fish) are primal and extremely connectable; they connect themselves up without much experience on the part of the chick and without any particular reinforcement or reward, as the psychologist commonly uses that concept. Flying patterns, which are more recently evolved than simple quadripedal locomotion, require more practice for their perfection and complete "hook up." As we have already seen, many sequences come already connected embryologically, and learning is merely an extension of those neurological processes that have been occurring embryologically or as the animal matures. The newer processes, such as manipulating parts of the environment to get food do not usually come completely hooked up, nor are they as easily connectable as the imprinting process, for example, whereby the baby duck learns to follow its mother. Newer processes, also, such as flying ability in birds, may be more easily lost in later evolutionary history—the emu, the ostrich, and the rhea may be cases in point, although whether they represent a loss or a failure to evolve is considered by some scholars debatable.

6. The more primitive parts of the organism's behavior are more persistent, less apt to die out (or extinguish) in the face of lack of success or lack of follow-through. For instance, if rats are allowed to mate to the point of intromission, they will not extinguish or give up trying, even though ejaculation is prevented. Also violent fears (arousals of the primitive flight patterns) that have occurred in the presence of certain features of the environment may last the

lifetime of the organism, even though persistent exposure to the same feature of the environment may show the animal he has no "reason" to fear.

7. Cycles and subcycles of behavior at the primal end are more stereotyped than those at the recent end. Each subcycle is more like the preceding and the following ones than in the case of the evolutionarily newer behavior cycles. Thus, each repeated swallowing sequence or cycle is more like the previous swallow than is each repeated manipulation or picking up of a piece of food, and swallows are considerably more like each other than such learned cycles as firing a gun, say.

8. Properties of learned, newer-type sequences tend to take on the properties of the older, more primal sequences as they become very well learned (overlearned). We have all noticed that well-learned behavior patterns require very little input from the environment for their control; you can walk through your house in the dark. A good driver may drive "automatically," without noticing the position of his foot on the accelerator or how far he turns the wheel to stay on the road, whereas the beginner requires careful attention to these parts of the environment. Also, overlearned sequences become more stereotyped as learning progresses. In the early stages of learning a piano piece, for example, repeated recycles of the same bar are much more varied and less like each other than later on when the student perfects the passage and achieves a rendition that suits him (and the teacher). We have already mentioned above (pages 32–33) how piano playing differs in other properties from a typical primal sequence.

CHAPTER III

Interpreting Experiments

PERHAPS NOW, WITH THIS OVERVIEW OF THE GENERAL
nature and properties of behavior, we are in a better position to look
at what is going on in the laboratory animal experiment (and in
other types of animal studies and observations). What do we see
now which we did not see before?

WHAT HAPPENS IN THE SKINNER BOX?

Probably the most widely used of all experimental situations for
studying animal behavior is the so-called Skinner box—a device
developed by B. F. Skinner, now of Harvard University, for the
experimental analysis of behavior. The results derived from experiments using rats in the original Skinner boxes culminated in 1938 in
Skinner's classic, *The Behavior of Organisms* (Skinner, 1938), and
since then countless modifications of the Skinner box, and countless
elaborations of Skinner's experiments have produced what is today
probably the predominant method of investigating animal behavior
in American laboratories. This method is known as operant or instrumental conditioning, and the theoretical structure is sometimes also
referred to as *neobehaviorism*, because, although basically behavioristic in outlook and methodology, it represents a "new look" when
compared to the original Watsonian behaviorism. (See reprint [3].)

Operant conditioning has had a tremendous influence, not only on
laboratory experimentation, but on the teaching and interpretation

of learning theory in psychology classes. It has also proved a tremendously useful tool in the practical control of animal and human behavior. Our original work with Dr. Skinner, and especially our experience with him on the famous guided missile project which used operantly conditioned pigeons (Skinner, 1960), was the inspiration for and starting point of our own development of the field of applied animal psychology (Breland and Breland, 1951). Operant conditioning methods have been successfully used in training severely retarded children (Southern Regional Educational Board, 1965) and, also in the human learning realm, underlie the now vast teaching machine and programed learning fields.

The early experiments, by Skinner and others, were done largely with white rats, and the rat is still the animal of choice for most experimenters. After the pigeon project, Skinner began making extensive use of the pigeon as a regular laboratory animal. Although lately other species have been studied with these methods, the range is still exceedingly small, and herein lie some of the pitfalls, both theoretical and practical, as we discovered to our sorrow (and expense) (Breland and Breland, 1961). Bitterman (1960, 1965) has fairly recently embarked on a determined program to extend studies of this sort to a wide range of species including fish, birds, and mammals.

At this point, the reader may find it useful to refer to the selection in the readings section from Keller and Schoenfeld's *Principles of Psychology* [3]. This selection describes in brief the history of operant psychology and delineates the basic methods and interpretations. The distinctions made here between operant and respondent conditioning have proved quite controversial, and the reader may want to reserve opinion on this matter until we have had a closer look. Elaborating, then, somewhat on the Keller and Schoenfeld description, let us see what the rat in the Skinner box is doing.

In conventional operant terms, the behavior of the rat in the Skinner box might be diagramed as follows:

$$s \longrightarrow R \longrightarrow S^D \longrightarrow R \longrightarrow S^R \longrightarrow R$$

s	R	S^D	R	S^R	R
(lever and surrounding stimuli)	press	click of feeder	runs to feeder	pellet	eats

Operant

In an expanded description: the lever and the whole area of the box itself provides the generalized stimulus situation (which later becomes an S^D, or discriminative stimulus, the signal to the animal that if he presses the lever he will be fed); the first R represents the response of pressing the lever; this is followed by the S^D, or discriminative stimulus of the sound of the feeder, the sign that if the rat runs to the feeder, he will find food there. The next R refers to the response of running to the feeder, where he finds the S^R (reinforcing stimulus), which he picks up and eats, thereby concluding the final R in the operant paradigm, or diagram of the "chain of responses."

To elaborate: without, at this point, starting too far back in history, we might describe the beginning point of the experiment as the night the experimenter took the food away from the rat. Instead of having food continuously available, the rat now gets nothing to eat, for about 24 hours. Then the experimenter takes the rat out of his home cage (usually by hand) and puts him in the Skinner box. Either there will be a pellet in the tray of the feeder, or soon after the rat is put in the box, the experimenter will operate the feeder (automatically or by hand) and drop the rat a pellet. If the rat is not too frightened, he will find the pellet and eat it. Then begins the regular sequence of what is known as "conditioning to the sound of the feeder." The experimenter starts a regular sequence consisting of operating the feeder, which usually makes a clicking or buzzing noise, thereby dropping a pellet, and allowing the rat to find and eat the pellet.

After the rat is thoroughly accustomed to the sound of the feeder and to finding and eating the pellets, the experimenter then connects the lever to the feeder so that the rat must depress the lever in order to work the feeder. From this point on pellets will not come regularly and automatically to the rat. He may go to the feed tray several times. He may sit for a while and do nothing. He may wash his face (an activity known to the ethologists as a "displacement" activity, of which more later). But because he is hungry, the chances are he will get up and start sniffing around and exploring the box. If in the course of these wanderings he happens upon the lever, climbs on it, or otherwise depresses it, the feeder will click, the rat will go to the tray (because he has already been conditioned to do so), and eat the pellet. After a few such experiences, sometimes after only one, especially if the lever is quite close to the tray, the rat will regularly press the lever, go to the feeder, eat, press the lever, go to the feeder, eat, and so on, at quite a steady rate, until he is full or until the experimenter removes him. The operant psychologist will now say that the rat is conditioned to press the lever for food reinforcement. The operant, "lever pressing," is occurring at a steady rate.

After the regular rate of lever pressing is achieved, the experimenter may go on to introduce countless variations in procedures—for example, after a stable rate is reached, the experimenter will perhaps start reinforcing only every other lever press, or every fourth one or an average of every six presses on a random schedule, or at one lever press every 30 seconds, and so on. The rat will continue to press the lever at a regular rate under most of these conditions, and records (similar to those pictured in Keller and Schoenfeld) will show fairly regular changes, depending on which one of these "schedules of reinforcement" is used.

Another procedure which the experimenter may institute is called "extinction." This is not described in the selection reprinted from Keller and Schoenfeld but is treated in detail in later portions of their book. In brief, the experimenter disconnects the lever from the feeder, so that pressing the lever now no longer delivers pellets to the pan. (Or the feeder is left empty, so that it sounds, but no pellets drop down.) Now the rat presses; if the feeder sounds, he goes to the pan; there is no pellet. Even if the feeder is disconnected so there is no sound, he may still go to the pan, or he may simply look in its direction. What does he do? The chances are he will immediately go back and press the lever and run to the pan again. He will undoubtedly, if he has been well conditioned, do this a large number of times, generally in a fast burst of activity. Then he will begin to slow down; he may stop, wash his face, run around the box, chew the pan, try to get out; he may even attack the lever savagely. This behavior (except direct attacks on the lever) will not result in recorded responses; the record will show "flat" spots. Then he may go back and try the lever again, run off a few bursts of sequences, then stop again and comb his whiskers. After a few such tries, he may even curl up and go to sleep. A cumulative curve of his lever pressing performance is shown on page 50 (Figure 1).

If the next day the experimenter puts the rat back in the box with the lever still disconnected (or the feeder empty), the rat will try again, even though he stopped completely the day before. He will run off another quick initial burst of sequences (this is known as "spontaneous recovery"), then stop, then perhaps run off a few more, and so on, but the chances are he will give up more quickly

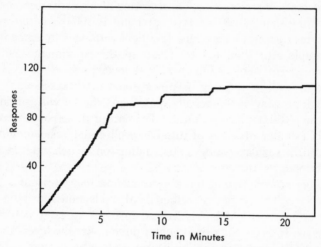

FIGURE 1. A typical extinction curve.

on this occasion. On the average each successive time the rat will give up more quickly. However, if the lever is again connected to the feeder (or the feeder refilled) the rat will again "condition" and start pressing the lever regularly, generally reaching a stable, steady rate more quickly than he did originally.

Another procedure the experimenter may use involves what is known as "discrimination." The experimenter may have the lever connected to the feeder only when a light is on, leaving it disconnected when the light is off. During the first day of such a procedure, the rat will no doubt continue to press the lever a considerable number of times in the dark; however, generally speaking, this tendency will decrease even during the first day of such "discrimination training"; the rat will gradually tend to press the lever only when the light is on, and the responses in the dark will drop off according to the typical fashion of the extinction curve. In other examples of discrimination studies, the experimenter may use two levers, with a triangle, for example, above one and a square above the other, and require that the animal press only the lever with the triangle above it in order to get a pellet. If he shifts the position of the triangle, he may, by studying the rat's records, be able to tell whether the rat can "tell the difference" between a triangle and a square. (Of course, if the experimenter did not shift the positions, he might only be able to tell that the rat was discriminating one lever position from another.)

The experimenter may also put weights on the lever, perhaps of successively greater weight, so that the rat has to press harder and harder in order to obtain the pellet. This process is known as "differentiation"—the rat (and the apparatus) differentiates between weak presses and hard ones.

Pavlov's Experiment

In the section reprinted from Pavlov's *Conditioned Reflexes* [2] the reader will find a basic description of Pavlov's methods and some of the principal results of his classic experiments, as well as his own interpretations of what is going on in the animal's nervous system and a number of observations concerning innate and reflex behavior, which the reader may now be able to relate to the background material we have tried to supply in the second chapter.

Pavlov was a Russian physiologist, and philosophically his heritage can be traced, as can that of the operanticists, to the mechanistic notions of Descartes, the French philosopher of the seventeenth century. The emphasis on stimulus control of the organism is very strong in Pavlovian thinking, and of course, it is this stimulus–response, push-pull view of the causation of behavior which was passed down through Watsonian behaviorism (Watson, 1924) to the neobehaviorists, and is preserved in the philosophical position of operant conditioning. As the reader can see, both positions are concerned largely with *learning;* a great deal of emphasis is placed on what goes on in the environment, on the control of the stimulus, on changes in behavior with the experience of the animal, on what goes on outside the skin. Although the operant psychologists have gone beyond a strict stimulus determinism in noting that "an operant must exist at some strength (prior to conditioning) in order to be emitted," there is a tendency to assume that the animal comes into the laboratory as a *tabula rasa* (blank slate) awaiting the impinge of the stimuli which the experimenter selects and that the ultimate control and determination of the organism's behavior lie in the outside world.

Also implicit are the assumptions that species differences are insignificant (this assumption, which rests partially on the Cartesian environmentalist–mechanist position, has been aggravated by the failure to study more than a very few species), that stimuli are freely interchangeable, from situation to situation and from organism to organism (the reader may note an expression to this effect in Pavlov's lecture), and that the choice of behavior sequences to be studied and the design of experimental situations may safely be left to the experimenter's taste—it will make no difference to the animal.

These assumptions are in the process of being challenged, both from outside the ranks of stimulus–response psychology (by the work of the ethologists, for example, Tinbergen, 1951, and Lorenz, 1952, and see reading [4], and from within by such researches as those of Bitterman (1960 and 1965), Olds (1956), and others. However, they still underlie and influence a vast quantity (as we have noted, probably the majority) of the research now being done in American psychological laboratories, and hence they cannot be ignored in any overview of the study of animal behavior.

In simple descriptive terms, what are the basic steps in the Pavlovian experiment? Without going back into the detailed history of how the experimenter prepares the animal for the series of actual experiments, we can start at the point where the hungry animal is placed in an elaborate harness designed to hold him virtually motionless and to which the recording equipment (and sometimes other pieces of equipment) can be attached. The laboratory is usually carefully soundproofed and isolated to keep out extraneous stimulation. The experimenter generally performs all procedures and keeps records from an adjoining room.

If a small amount of meat powder is now introduced into the dog's mouth, saliva will flow through a tube inserted through the side of the dog's mouth, and the recording equipment will note the number of drops. Now the experimenter may arrange it so that repeatedly a stimulus (a ticking metronome, a bell, a light, and so on) is introduced near the dog simultaneously with or just before the administration of the meat powder. After several pairings of this so-called conditioned stimulus (the metronome, and so on) with the unconditioned stimulus (the meat powder), the presentation of the conditioned stimulus alone will cause the dog to salivate.

This is the basic observation, and again, variations on the experiment are many: the experimenter may note the course of extinction; for example, if the conditioned reflex (salivation to the metronome alone) is elicted a number of times without reinforcement (application of or pairing with the meat powder), the conditioned reflex will gradually weaken and after a while will not occur. The experimenter may also study discrimination processes—he may reinforce with meat powder a certain stimulus, such as a tone of a certain frequency, and fail to administer the meat powder at another frequency. If the conditioned reaction occurs to the first tone but not to the second, it is clear that the animal can tell the difference between the two tones.

The Keller and Schoenfeld selection gives a description of the various differences in the two procedures known sometimes as Pavlovian or respondent, and instrumental or operant conditioning. Let us now examine the experimental situations in the light of our earlier revolutionary and organismic overview.

A New Outlook on the Two Conditioning Experiments

We have gone through the conventional descriptions of what goes on in the Skinner box situation and in the Pavlovian experiment. However, from a deeper organismic level, a great deal can be added. Remembering that the animal is "designed" by his evolutionary history to do business in a certain ecological niche, we can look now at the rat and the dog and the artificial ecological niches that the experimenters have provided and view them in a fresh light.

Consider first the Skinner box "niche": in the first place, when the experimenter took the food pan away from the rat's living cage, he interrupted the rat's normal eating cycles. The rat could no longer go through his normal eating behavior, either at the externally obvious level of seeking food, picking it up and ingesting it, or at the more primal level of swallowing, digesting, and assimilating it. He was compelled to stay in his cage, getting hungrier and hungrier—his internal processes having to do with nutrition becoming more and more activated. This, then, is the basis of the "hunger drive"— the interruption of the eating sequences, and it can occur either artificially, by the intervention of the experimenter, for example, or it can occur naturally, by physical barriers, scarcity of food, and so on.

Now the experimenter puts the rat in the Skinner box; this is an odd sort of ecological niche for a rat, of course, but if he is not too emotionally upset (if his tendencies to try to run away are not too highly aroused), by running around and sniffing (a normal enough type of food-getting sequence), he may come upon the pellet that the experimenter has provided in the food tray. If left with a whole pan of pellets, a hungry rat will merely seize, chew, swallow, seize, chew, swallow. We should also point out that as the rat seizes the food and chews, he also salivates, and of course, each cycle continues on down farther as we have seen. This sequence will recycle until the rat is full. But again the experimenter has interrupted the cycle by withholding the second pellet. What then happens?

The rat may sniff, wander about, explore, scan. These are ancient evolutionary patterns, it is true, but not as old as ingestion and digestion, and in the rat's case they may use many pieces of physiological and psychological "equipment" that are fairly new in evolutionary time—eyes, vibrissae, and so on.

If the rat has been properly conditioned to the sound of the feeder, when it clicks and drops another pellet, the rat will reel off the last links of the sequence: he will run to the feeder, seize (and salivate), chew, swallow. We now have a sequence of patterns consisting of eating, chewing, swallowing, going away, returning, eating, chewing, swallowing, and so on.

Again the experimenter interrupts the sequence. He does not administer any more "free" pellets, but connects the lever to the feeder. In order to get the pellet, another link must be added to the sequence—again a link that involves evolutionarily newer processes (even more so than approach to the food): he must somehow (by climbing, foot movements, bumping it with his nose, or the like) depress the lever, and must *learn* that pressing the lever will be followed by the action of the feeder.

Now when the rat presses the lever, the feeder drops a pellet of food. The rat approaches the feeder, picks up the pellet, ingests it, chews it, swallows it, digests it, assimilates it. The food is customarily spoken of as a reinforcer, and we say in operant-conditioning terminology that lever-pressing behavior has been reinforced. However a more fundamental statement is to say that the behavior sequence is reinforced when that sequence (lever pressing) and a part of the environment (the lever connection to the feeder) interact to *bridge the interruption of an evolutionarily older (more primal) sequence (approaching the food) and allow it to resume its cycle.*

In the case of the Pavlovian experiment, again the experimenter starts with a hungry animal—in this case usually a dog. The dog has been deprived of food for a certain number of hours, and the internal sequences having to do with nutrition have been activated. In his pen, living cage, or kennel, he was, as was the rat, prevented from going through his normal food-getting sequences. Furthermore, when brought into the laboratory, the dog suffers even more interruptions of his normal food-getting patterns than does the rat. Not only is he deprived of his hunting grounds and the ordinary sources of food available to a dog—he is also confined in a harness, so that he is effectively prevented from doing almost anything with his skeletal musculature. This is certainly an extraordinary "ecological niche" for a hungry animal.

In addition, the stimuli from the surrounding room and building are cut to an absolute minimum. No normal sounds of the dog's life (or even abnormal ones that might interfere with the experiment) are permitted. However, this does not mean that *no* stimuli are present. The overall situation in the Pavlovian laboratory (except for the harness) does not differ appreciably from the interior of the Skinner box, as far as the dog is concerned. Indeed, Skinner boxes are also usually soundproofed, dark, and as free from extraneous stimulation as is practically possible.

Now if the experimenter introduces into the mouth of the hungry dog a bit of meat powder, he "plugs into" part of the normal ingestive behavior of the animal (which as we have seen is already "hot" and ready to go)—the dog will salivate and swallow. If the experimenter then adds to the already existing stimulation coming from the laboratory surroundings such a stimulus input as a bell or a metronome and pairs it with the meat powder, as we have seen, sooner or later the dog will come to salivate when the bell alone (with the additional stimuli of the surroundings), without the meat powder, is presented. Again we have reinforcement occurring, not by a *thing*, the meat powder, but by the resumption of an interrupted sequence.

Now it cannot be said that the bell, metronome, or other such stimulus is a completely "neutral" stimulus for the dog before this pairing occurs. If it were completely neutral, it would not be a stimulus for the dog at all—the dog wouldn't even be able to hear it! To any such sound, the dog will make various types of reactions —any of the appropriate sort which he can make, strapped down as he is: he may prick up his ears, he may turn his head toward the sound, certain of his body muscles may stiffen. These sequences are then followed by the meat powder, which in turn fires off the salivating and swallowing, and so on down the line. The orienting reactions to the bell are thus reinforced or strengthened because they are followed by more primal sequences connected with ingestion.

It should now be possible for us to begin to see that there are scant differences here between the Pavlovian

$$\text{lab plus bell} \longrightarrow \text{orienting sequences} \longrightarrow \text{meat powder} \longrightarrow \text{salivation} \longrightarrow$$

and the operant situation:

$$\text{Skinner box plus light} \longrightarrow \text{orienting sequences} \longrightarrow \text{lever pressing} \longrightarrow \text{pellet} \longrightarrow \text{salivation} \longrightarrow$$

When the response is well conditioned the paradigm looks like this:

$$\text{Skinner box plus light} \longrightarrow \text{orienting sequences} \longrightarrow \text{lever pressing salivation} \longrightarrow \text{pellet} \longrightarrow$$

because as Shapiro has shown (1960, 1961), once conditioned the animal salivates when he presses the lever.

The only difference is that in the operant situation the experimenter adds the contingency that the rat must press the lever; this requirement is missing in the Pavlovian situation, so that the dog's operant behavior undergoes extinction. However, as much overt activity as possible occurs in the strapped-down dog, and a careful observational program would no doubt reveal that certain muscular sequences were being "superstitiously" conditioned in the Pavlovian situation, just as zoo animals will often form extraneous and unnecessary sequences such as hopping onto the roof of the cage as the feed cart comes along, even though the hopping does nothing to hasten the food or produce it; also pigeons who have been conditioned to peck a plate when a light is on and whose pecking has been extinguished when the light is off may form such "superstitions" as turning in circles just before the light come on (Skinner, 1948). It is easy to see how such fortuitous movements become conditioned: once or twice by accident the pigeon turns in a circle just before the light is due to come on—thus circling is followed by the opportunity to peck the plate and in turn by eating.

The two types of experiments are simply concerned with different aspects of the same sort of ingestive sequences in mammals. The Pavlovian experimenter is concentrating on some of the more primal sequences (in fact, Pavlov started out by studying even more primal sequences—namely, stomach secretions) while the operant investigator is working farther up the line with evolutionarily newer, skeletal behavior sequences. The same processes go on; sequences are interrupted and resumed; reinforcement takes place when sequences are allowed to go to completion and to tack onto more primal sequences. They are all part and parcel of the same type of organismic activity.

Fresh Definitions of Conditioning Concepts

Looking at conventional concepts in this new light, we have seen that for a "reinforcement" to occur, an interrupted sequence must be allowed to go to completion, or the behavior sequences must merge into, move into the direction of, or "tack onto" evolutionarily older sequences. Thus reinforcement involves a progressive change from the evolutionarily newer (neoteric) to the older or more primal sequences. Reinforcement involves a natural regression to older ways and retraces in a general way the evolutionary history of the animal all the way back to the synthesis of protein molecules, the pairing of gametes, and so on. In short, reinforcement is regressive, and regression is reinforcing. This is true in a much more general sense than Freud intended, although Freudian regression (where the organism regularly and consistently employs more primal or more infantile modes of behavior) is a special case. In such cases the organism's more advanced and newer systems have, for various reasons, perhaps, failed; or the organism is under extreme stress (and as we have noted above, extreme stress strengthens the primal sequences relatively more than it does the neoteric); or both. At any rate, for one or more of these reasons the organism does not recycle his behavior sequences through the evolutionarily newer sequences but stays consistently regressed to the more primal level.

It is important to note that the resumption of *any* interrupted sequence is reinforcing, so that we can talk about the "drive" to finish a tune, the urge to complete a job, the reinforcing effect of being allowed to finish something once it is begun, the expectant, waiting feeling when the other shoe has not been dropped, and so on (Ovsiankina, 1928).

Learned sequences in general apparently show the same properties as the instinctive behaviors, an additional point that strengthens the position that the innate–learned dichotomy is an artificial one. Also, any sequence of behavior, learned or innate, can reinforce any other sequence, so long as the reinforcing one is a sequence followed by older sequences, whether learned or not. Note that the reinforcing process is in the behavior sequence itself, and is not an object, a stimulus, or a piece of the environment. So in the Skinner box situation, it is not the pellet of food that reinforces going to the pan (or lever pressing); it would be more accurate to say that going to the pan reinforces lever pressing; picking up the food reinforces going to the pan; ingesting the food reinforces picking it up; salivating, chewing, and swallowing reinforce ingestion; digestive and assimilative processes reinforce salivating, chewing, and swallowing. Like other aspects of behavior, reinforcement processes obviously are ultimately traceable in higher animals to the action of the central nervous system, as Olds (1956) has shown in his experiments.

To elaborate on the problem of drive: the condition known as *drive*, or motivation, occurs in an organism when a sequence is interrupted. These interruptions can occur for various reasons. In the case of the so-called primary drives, such as hunger and sex, the interruptions are internal or endogenous, and occur because of interruptions in endogenous processes; we have already seen how this process works in the case of the hungry raccoon and the hungry rat, whose internal assimilative and digestive processes are activated but cannot go on to completion because they have been blocked or interrupted by newer processes (mediated, as we have seen, in the higher animals, by the newer parts of the nervous system) which "tell" the animal, "The signs are not right; there is nothing here to assimilate."

Fear, avoidance, escape from punishment involve "drives" that occur as a result of environmentally induced interruptions of behavior sequences. Situations that induce fear, "punishing" situations, are basically those that fire off the flight or escape patterns of the organism. These escape patterns are interruptive because they interfere with the behavior sequences that have to do with the basic "appetitive" functions of the organism—the primary assignments concerned with assimilation and reproduction. These, as we have seen, are the organism's first concern: he must maintain his cellular and molecular integrity, and he must reproduce his kind. You can see from this that escape and avoidance are secondary processes. An organism cannot go around escaping all the time. He must eat and he must mate (or otherwise reproduce); however, there are occasions when in order to maintain his molecular integrity he must escape from someone who wants to eat him (or some other environmental condition, such as a storm, fire, flood, cold, or heat), or remove a part of his body from some similar threat to its integrity, and when these occasions arise, the escape sequences will usually interrupt the sequences having to do with eating or mating. It is in this sense that we can say that the removal of an aversive stimulus (a condition which fires off escape sequences) is reinforcing, because this removal allows the organism to resume the basic ongoing sequences having to do with eating, mating, and so on.

Situations involving avoidance and punishment may also contain a secondary block or interruption. Suppose that the animal's flight sequences have been fired off, or aroused, at least—the animal has been startled, by a loud sound, the sight of a predator, or, as often happens in a laboratory experiment, by an electric shock. The animal gets ready to flee; now, if he is prevented from escaping by physical restraints, as in the laboratory box or harness, we are dealing with a double interruption: endogenous drives that may have been activated, such as hunger, have been interrupted by the shock (or noise, or other), and flight sequences, externally aroused, have been interrupted by barriers. Under these conditions, the sequences having to do with flight or escape will remain continually aroused (resulting in "fear" or "anxiety") and partially activated until escape is possible or the occasion that aroused them in the first place is removed. In such a case we might say not that the animal is afraid because he is running, but because he cannot run, in contrast to the old James–Lange theory (Woodworth, 1938, pages 242 and 273), which held that the fear was part of, or because of, the running away or other motor patterns.

What of the concept of the *stimulus*, which we have mentioned in connection with these experimental descriptions and more generally in our "long" look at organismic processes? We have already observed that reaction to stimulation, sense organs, and the parts and processes to deal with inputs from the environment are evolutionarily newer developments that serve the older parts and processes of the organism and make it possible for him to do commerce with a complex environment. Furthermore, the higher and newer animals can handle a much greater variety of environmental input than can the lower organisms, which generally react only to very restricted types and ranges of physical impingements.

Species come equipped to recognize or react to only certain inputs or portions of the environment. There can be no input without a certain impingement from the environment, and there can be no intake without an "accepting" process in the organism. This accepting process is definitely concerned with nervous structure and function, both with end organ (eye, ear, taste buds, and other receptive cells) and with central nervous system processes, and its nature is beyond the scope of this book. However, we think we can say without question that any ultimate resolution or explanation of the problems of muscular integrations, sensory reception, and learning will take place by advances in neurology. For the most part, the psychologist has largely "skirted" the nervous system, but as the experiments of von Holst (1962), Penfield (1959), and others have shown, the nervous system is the immediate and proximal determiner as far as muscular patterning is concerned—stimulation applied through an electrode into a certain spot in the brain will produce in the organism the patterned unreeling of a definite sequence of movements.

Typically the psychologist has started with the outside world and its effect on the organism. However, it must be remembered that the organism both ontologically and in an evolutionary sense at first is only able to deal with effects of the outside world in a very gross sense, then improves the specificity of its reception, and by the nature of its characteristics and processes determines what will be the nature of the stimuli to which it can react. The acceptor has to develop before a stimulus can occur. If there is no acceptor, there is no stimulus. Therefore, the organism—not the psychologist—defines the stimulus. There is no way that a psychologist can define a stimulus except that an organism can "take it in," accept it, react to it.

Acceptor patterns may be learned or innate. An animal may innately accept certain inputs as indicating food, or something with which to fight or to mate, or it may learn that a certain whistle, for example, emitted by a human, means, "Come get your pan of dog food"—obviously learned acceptor patterns, for human whistles or pans would have little significance for the original dogs. Here again the dichotomy between what is learned and what is innate makes little sense. Again we are dealing with a continuum of connectability, conditionability, learnability. Some acceptor patterns are much easier to acquire than others.

Thus, we are once more in the position of having to reemphasize the internal nature of the determination of most organismic behavior. Although it would be very convenient if the stimulus could be physically and objectively defined and if the control and determination of the organism could be placed unequivocally in the external world, unfortunately this is not possible.

For any stimulus situation of the external world that is effective for a given organism (to which he reacts at all), that makes any difference in his behavior, the animal has an acceptor pattern "somewhere" or somehow in his nervous system. The dog has acceptor patterns for the sights, sounds, and smells of Pavlov's laboratory. Conditioning a discriminative stimulus, such as the bell, simply adds an element (or two or more) to the acceptor pattern. It is clear, too, that the internal condition of the organism determines the effect of stimulus inputs: the conditions of the animal's acceptors change with the animal's chemical balance, state of fatigue or excitement, body temperature, and so on, as has been shown by extensive experiments on lower organisms (Maier and Schneirla,

1964, pages 88–90). Thus an earthworm in different stages from rest to extreme excitement gives a succession of different responses to the same type of stimulus.

THE LABORATORY NICHE

In each case, when an animal is placed in a situation that differs from its native habitat, whether in a Skinner box, a maze, or some other type of laboratory situation, we would do well to look closely to see how the new situation compares with the animal's normal environment. If there are important differences, how will these affect the animal's behavior, both with respect to the type of activity being studied and with respect to other behavior that may also become activated. Is this situation one, for example, that may tend to activate the animal's flight sequences? For example, suppose we take a free-flying bird and enclose it in a box. What does this do to the bird's escape tendencies? Then we require a bird, which happens to be a seed eater, to pull a string to activate the feeder. What is apt to happen? Does this bird, in its ordinary ecological niche, pull strings or objects like strings, in the course of food gathering? If not, what effect will this have on the experiment?

Secondly, we need to study the experiment to note what primal sequences are being blocked. Nutritional? Other? After this has been determined, we should note what provisions are made for the animal to "long-circuit"—to get around the blocks or interruptions and resume the sequences to completion and consequent reinforcement. How closely do these conditions correspond to similar conditions in the animal's native environment? How do the patterns required by the conditions of the experiment correspond to the animal's built-in instinctive patterns?

When we have learned to look at animals and research in this light, some experiments—for example, those dealing with punishment—reveal features that were not before apparent. All such experiments have certain striking features in common. First, punishment or threat of punishment tends to activate the animal's escape behavior. Consider now the almost universal initial response of an animal in the wild to a warning or a danger signal. Usually his first response is not to break out into wild flight but to stop, look, and listen. Thus the first behavior sequence is most often the "freeze," with the animal alert—listening, sniffing, looking, trying to evaluate the significance of the sensory input. Depending then on what his senses tell him, the animal may sneak silently off through the brush, may freeze and stay put, or may break into wild flight. Which happens depends on the situation and on the animal in question. For the animal with protective coloration, the best bet is to stay hidden in the sun-dappled leaves; for the ungulate without cover on the open prairie, the best bet is rapid flight, but he first chooses his direction.

The typical laboratory experiment involving punishment or threat of punishment is conducted in a very restricted area—a closed box or small pen. Sometimes the animal is even strapped down. A light or tone or buzzer often signals the onset of a shock—the most common "punishment" in such experiments. When the shock is applied, the animal tries to escape, but if he is boxed in or tied down, he cannot do so. His normal escape behavior is violently activated, but he has no natural "out." Some experimental situations, of course, do give the animal a semblance of such natural escape—barriers to jump over, platforms to jump onto, and so on. But when a pigeon is required to peck a key to turn off a shock, the bird is faced with a completely unnatural situation and fails to learn the task required. The last thing a bird should be doing when faced with danger is to be pecking around at spots. A chance to fly onto a perch would produce dramatic changes in the character of this type of experiment.

The preeminent use of shock in punishment experiments is itself a questionable procedure. An electric shock is a highly unnatural punishment. Where in the wild would an animal encounter such a demon? Furthermore, shock is difficult to control and to administer uniformly. The combination produces a situation that is very difficult to interpret in terms of an animal's ongoing behavior. Certainly some effort ought to be made to find more natural punishing or fear-inducing situations to use in the study of punishment and its avoidance.

Many such natural punishing situations do occur in ordinary laboratory situations, and although they are not so interpreted by the experimenter, they may be by the animal. For example, handling, especially of animals that have been raised without human contact to near maturity, can be a very traumatizing experience to an animal. The experimenter probably does not consider when he picks up a rat or a bird and puts it in an experimental chamber that he is punishing the animal, but the animal often has a different viewpoint. In essence, the animal is being grabbed by a predator. Many laboratory experimentalists bear tooth marks on their fingers to testify as to what the rat "thinks" of the situation. Even animals that have been thoroughly domesticated and raised with people from an early age may, when picked up, struggle to avoid the clutching hand. Young ducks and chickens, for example, do not care to be handled, and will get away if they can. In their society, friends are not grabbers.

Other interpretive problems have not always been reported in the literature, but have turned up in conversations. For example, we have talked often with research workers who have been using the cat as an experimental animal. Very commonly the initial stages of their experiments have presented considerable problems. Frequently this experimental apoplexy is caused by requiring that the cat work a manipulandum, lever, switch, string, or what-have-you, at the *opposite* end of the experimental chamber from the feeder. This requirement is grossly contrary to the cat's nature. Generally the cat spends some time—often several experimental sessions—simply attacking the source of the food instead of doing the simple and logical thing (which a self-respecting rat would probably do within the first experimental hour); furthermore, the hungrier the cat gets, the more it attacks the feeder. (As we have seen, extreme stress activates more primitive sequences, and direct attack is more primitive than ranging out for food.)

Of course, the cat in the wild simply does not get fed by going away from the source of his food; he solves his nutritional problems by direct attack on the prey. If you ask him to do anything else, you are putting unnecessary obstacles in the way of your experiment—unless you particularly want to study this sort of problem. For quick and facile conditioning, the manipulandum should be as close to the feeder as possible and arranged so that a direct food-getting response on the part of the cat will work the feeder. If the experiment requires the cat to work a manipulandum at some distance from the feeder, the transition should be made gradually. The manipulandum should be moved gradually away from the feeder to successively greater distances. Grossman (1965) has had some interesting observations to make about the differences between cats and such herbivores as rabbits, and the general role of apparatus in experimental results. (See also page 115.)

Much as the rat has been studied by behavioral scientists, interpretive problems still arise. Consider, for example, "spontaneous alternation," in the T maze. In simplest form, something like the following happens: when a rat is presented with two equally long paths to food and, for example, turns right, on the next run the rat may perversely turn left. The tendency is toward consistent alternation. This naturally produces great interpretive consternation. Why should the rat turn left when it has found food by turning right? First, consider the nature and magnitude of the reinforcement. Rats in their wild state often feast upon great hordes of food. In their present-day ecological niche, which they occupy so successfully alongside agricultural man, they may dig into a granary and drag home a whole ear of corn, which would last one rat a long time, or gnaw a hole in a sack of wheat. To run a labyrinth and encounter only a tiny bit of food at the end might be a pretty good indication to the rat to try the other path next time. Secondly, the rat makes his living by exploring dark corridors; unless there are overwhelming reasons for taking the right turn always, it may be to his advantage in the long run to try a new way to see what may lie at the end of it, even though he has had some success in the other direction.

Another interpretive problem has arisen in a class of experiments indicating that a rat in a darkened chamber will readily learn to press a lever to turn on a dim light but not to turn on a bright one. This is, again, not very surprising when we consider the rat's normal living conditions. The rat's burrow is a place of Stygian darkness; in order to make a living, the rat must leave this darkness and go, not into the bright sunlight, for he is a nocturnal creature, but into dimly illuminated areas. Thus, a dim light at the end of a dark area is the normal situation that leads to the rat's hunting, which leads to food (and we have already seen how sequences that lead into more primal sequences are reinforcing).

The rat is also guilty of posing the "latent learning" problem.

The basic observation here is that the "unmotivated" rat, not hungry or thirsty, when allowed to amble through a maze, may spend a number of trials showing little or no improvement in the time or error scores. Then suddenly, when the rat is allowed to become hungry and is given food at the end of the maze, there will be an abrupt drop in time-and-error scores instead of a gradual transition. Two assumptions commonly made about these experiments are interpretive pitfalls: first, that the rat is "unmotivated," and second, that conditioning is not taking place, that the rat is not being reinforced in these early trials.

One thing we can certainly say immediately: if the rat runs the maze at all he is motivated. There is a drive of some sort. It is simply a question of determining experimentally what sequences have been blocked. One possibility is the existence of subhungers. A rat can be fed to satiation on laboratory chow and still, as we know, possess subhungers for a great variety of other foods. Chickens fed to satiation on egg pellets will often eat corn and green grass, and we know ourselves that we may eat our fill of ordinary food and still have room left for dessert. However, subhungers are not necessarily the variables here. It is also true that the rat when placed in the maze is in unfamiliar territory, and perhaps actually nothing more need be aroused than a tendency to get back to familiar territory. Although the completion of the maze may not lead immediately to this fulfillment, still the activation of the sequences is there to set the rat running.

Also if we follow the interpretation of reinforcement given in the previous chapter—namely, that reinforcement occurs when interrupted sequences are allowed to go to completion—we can see that conditioning is going on at choice points in the early stages of the maze running, even though the rat is unrewarded with food at the end of the maze, if sequences are allowed to go to completion or they are blocked by the cul-de-sacs, or blind alleys. In addition, it is not to the rat's advantage in the wild to be caught in cul-de-sacs, and there may be some tendency to learn to avoid them on this basis. However, it would be sufficient to explain the fact that errors do not drop out more rapidly in the early unmotivated stages to postulate simply that the rat is becoming, on successive trials, more familiar with the maze and much less fearful of the cul-de-sacs,. so that exploration or locomotive sequences activated by other drive conditions are proceeding with less fear of the strangeness of the situation. But, in any case, the conditioning of the choice points that allow sequences to continue uninterrupted goes on, and when the food is suddenly introduced, the hungry rat can then take advantage of this preconditioning.

Another class of experiments that we are sure must have presented problems to many experimenters, although these problems are not always reported in the literature, are those requiring the animal to pick up an article and deposit it into a slot or container. B. F. Skinner encountered this difficulty in his classic experiment on Pliny, the rat that was shown and described in *Life* magazine (May 31, 1937). Pliny had a great deal of difficulty letting go of a marble to deposit it in a chute. We have, ourselves, repeatedly run into this problem with a great variety of animals—raccoons, monkeys, otters, pigs, and the like. In the case of a raccoon who was being conditioned to pick up a wooden egg and drop it down a chute, the raccoon at first dropped the egg promptly and went immediately to the feeder to secure his bite of food. However, the second time, the raccoon was extremely reluctant to drop the egg. He kept it in his hand, pulled it back out, looked at it, fondled it, put it back in the chute, pulled it back out again, and so on; this went on for several seconds. You might assume here that you were encountering only the raccoon's native fondness for eggs, but similarly otters trained to drop a wooden ball down a chute become very reluctant to let it go. They will paw over it, mouth it, chew it, and finally with great reluctance let it go. Pigs who have been conditioned to put large metal or wooden dollars in a piggy bank start out doing this neatly and with great precision. They pick up a dollar, put it in the bank, pick up another one, deposit it, and so on. But, after several weeks of performance, the behavior will gradually begin to change. The pig will root the coin, mouth it, toss it, and experience a great deal of difficulty and delay in depositing the coin in the bank. Squirrel monkeys have similarly been observed to be very reluctant to let go of coins when they have been rewarded with food for depositing them in a slot. This procedure actually delays the presentation of the food and is contrary to what would be expected by more conventional conditioning theory.

Because not much is known of the native wild behaviors of the raccoon, it is a little difficult to say what is going on. However, it is possible that the behavior in question is similar to that used by a raccoon in cracking a shell off a crayfish, opening a clam, and so on. The resemblance of the object in the raccoon's hand to a natural food object, followed by the appearance of broken-up food (such as dog pellets) makes it virtually certain that the behavior appropriate to similar articles in the raccoons' wild state will appear. In the case of the pig, we know a little bit more of what is going on. Pigs, in the wild, often kill small rodents and other small animals; the behavior exhibited by the pig with the disc is similar to that shown by a pig who has rooted up a field mouse and is tossing it and rooting it, killing it prior to eating it.

These problem sequences, of course, owe part of their troublesome nature to their evolutionary age; because of their essentially primal nature, they tie in very tightly and ineradicably to the situation.

The problem here occurs, as we have noted, after manipulating the object in question has been followed with food reinforcement. The object becomes virtually a food surrogate to the animal; he becomes more and more reluctant to let it go but treats it like a piece of food. This results in some cases in animals actually ingesting the object. For example, at one time we were endeavoring to teach turkeys to deposit coins in a bank. They did quite nicely at first; after a few days, however, the money began disappearing—we discovered that all of our profits were going into the turkeys, even coins as large as quarters. Again, this phenomenon occurred only after considerable association of the coins with food reinforcement. Later on, we decided to eat one of the turkeys; when we opened up its gizzard, we found coins worn virtually paper thin by the action of the gizzard.

This tendency of an object to become a food surrogate may have cost the life of one of Marineland of Florida's best porpoises, Algae, who had been taught to play baseball. Everything was going fine for several weeks; the ball was being thrown into the pool, and Algae would chase it and throw it back to the batter, who would bat it back out on the water to Algae. Then one day when Algae went to get the ball and came back to the trainer, there was no ball. The trainer looked all over the pool bottom, but found no trace of it. The conclusion was inescapable; Algae had swallowed it. Unfortunately, very little was known about veterinary procedures with the porpoise at that time, and while the veterinarians were trying to extract the ball, the porpoise died of shock. Subsequently a whale at Marineland of California swallowed an innertube, again following food reinforcement for retrieving the innertube. However, in this case a whale-sized dose of mineral oil led the whale to burp the tube back up again, and all was well. Although there may be other reasons for animals swallowing inedible objects, this sort of experience indicates the need for extreme caution in using experimental objects the manipulation of which is followed by feeding and which can be swallowed by an animal.

These are only a few examples of the design of experiments taking into consideration the behavioral characteristics of the animal. We think it is probably true that by now where experimenters have been familiar with the animals for a considerable period of time and have used fairly standard experimental situations, most have become fairly adept at designing experiments to fit the animal. The rat and the pigeon and many of the primates are rather well known now, and experimental apparatus has gone through many stages of construction and reconstruction to fit the animals in question. The maze has certainly been a "natural" for the rat although less suitable for college sophomores and particularly for pigeons. Indeed the differential suitability of apparatus to various species often makes interspecies comparisons completely invalid. However, when a new piece of apparatus is introduced or a new species, there is always the danger that something may go awry if the person who designed the apparatus did not know quite enough about the animal in question to design the apparatus properly. The pitfalls are many, and they can be avoided by a few basic procedures—a thorough study of the animal in question before a commitment to hardware is made, and flexibility of design so that preliminary apparatus can be constructed cheaply and quickly and tried out before expensive apparatus is constructed to no avail.

IV

Observational Data
on Animal Species

THE OBSERVATIONAL METHOD IS BECOMING MORE AND more respected in behavior research. The observations of the skilled field naturalist have, for many years, added greatly to our understanding of the behavior in the wild. The imaginative work of the ethologists has increased the flexibility and usefulness of the observational methods by adding the dimension of field experimentation—altering conditions deliberately to test out the variables in the animal's behavior. (See reprint [4].) We have mentioned, for example, the substitution of various articles to determine what fires off the fighting behavior of the male robin. In this case, it was determined that a red patch on a piece of cotton tuft would be sufficient to release the fighting behavior. In any case, it can safely be said that the observational method adds an important dimension to the information collected by careful experimentation, and should often be used as a preliminary before the design of laboratory experiments.

During the past 18 years, we have had the opportunity to observe under controlled or partially controlled conditions the behavior of more than 8,000 animals, representing over 60 different species. Some of these animals have been the subjects of more or less formal conditioning experiments. Others have been subjects for our development of the technology of animal behavior, which we described in our "Field of Applied Animal Psychology" (Breland and Breland, 1951).

Much of this work has been primarily engineering in character and thus, with a few exceptions, not strictly experimental. You might say that it lies somewhere between the realm of laboratory psychology and the observational methods of the ethologist.

These animals for the most part have been in much more informal experimental situations than those typical of the usual laboratory experiment. In general, our situation is characterized by more variety and freedom all around. Both the animal and man are free to exhibit behaviors and behavioral properties that must of a necessity be eliminated in the experimental laboratory. The great bulk of the data are primarily observational and not meticulously recorded in most instances. As behavioral engineers we have, of course, been more concerned with the specifications of outcome than with the rigor of method. In many cases these preliminary observations should be regarded as pointing to areas for experimentation. They are not always quantified nor is their interpretation always clearcut. However, we have observed many different animals and have learned great speed and flexibility in approaching problems. Thus, we feel the observations are of considerable value in the understanding of animal behavior in general and that our interpretive hunches stand generally on pretty firm ground. It has been largely this observational material, plus the considerable background reading we found necessary in order to make sense out of the behavior of our animals, that led us to the naturalistic evolutionary theoretical look at behavior which we have just presented.

With this discussion of the nature of our observations in mind and keeping always in mind our way of looking at behavior, let us take a look at some of the species we have had occasion to observe and describe some of the things we have learned about their behavior which, so far as we know, have never been reported in the ordinary experimental literature. Again, however, some excellent work is being done in animal husbandry and biology departments (Hafez, 1962).

There are many ways of classifying and subdividing such material. One of the logical ones would seem to be in terms of groups of related species or species that are related in behavioral fashions.

One of the important classifications of animal behavior concerns the animal's ecological niche and the way he customarily makes a living. Fitting into one niche, according to this classification, are the herbivorous mammals of various orders, genera, and species: rabbits and ungulates—for example, cattle, goats, sheep, deer, and horses.

THE HERBIVORES: RABBITS

We have worked with several hundred rabbits of several different breeds or varieties. Our earlier experiences were not notably successful, because in most cases at that time we were using the readily available heavy meat breeds, such as the New Zealand whites and California smut nose. One of these experiments ended in near disaster for the pair of smut-nose rabbits, because in spite of their extreme hunger we were not able to get them to cross a two-foot cage to pull a dowel for food. They simply lay on the cage floor. Although we wiggled the dowel, put rabbit food on it, and smeared it with syrup, nothing availed. Apparently in the process of domestication, the tendency to explore for food has been completely bred out of these strains. They simply vegetate, sit in a corner, and put on weight. They have enormous appetites and eat well, a little at a time, when the food is before them, but they simply will not put out any effort to obtain it. Since that time we have gone to a more active breed of rabbit, the belted Dutch, which we now raise ourselves, having selected them for activity and tameness.

Apparently rabbits rely very little on visual cues in finding their way around, although probably the pink-eyed albinos are even less dependent on their feeble eyesight than the darker-eyed strains. An early experiment in teaching rabbits to jump a hurdle demonstrated rather dramatically their reliance on spatial and kinesthetic cues. (One of these, incidentally, was pink-eyed and the other brown-eyed; both exhibited the same type of behavior.) A simple hurdle was constructed in the training pen by putting an up-ended two-by-four across the middle of it. To get from one end of the pen to the other, then, the rabbit had to hop over the two-by-four. Because the rabbit was fed alternately at each end of the pen, he soon learned to jump back and forth quite readily. However, we then decided they were ready for a higher hurdle, and added a second up-ended two-by-four to form a hurdle about eight inches high. The results were disconcerting to us, and no doubt, to the rabbit, because instead of jumping the barrier neatly, he rammed into it with his sensitive nose until this sad member was a bit bruised and scratched. (Since the pen was about eight feet long, he got up a fair amount of speed, and of course, there is a good deal of power in the rabbit's hind legs to propel the jump, and in this case, to propel his nose into the board.) Finally, the rabbit stopped, raised up, sniffed along the top of the second two-by-four, eventually apparently learning the extent of the change, for hereafter he cleared the top. It seemed that he had not seen the barrier at all, but was gauging the height of his jump on the basis of place and muscle sense—aiming for the same spot in the air, regardless of visual cues. When a third two-by-four was added, the same performance was repeated.

In our open tabletop experiments, using a hand-held cup feeder with a clicker, we had similar experiences. Most of our previous work had been with chickens. With them, presenting objects in various locations on the tabletop had little affect, but in such a shifting situation, the rabbit was completely lost. He was very slow to find the feed cup when it was moved about, and it was extremely difficult for him to locate manipulanda when they were moved around the table. Even seemingly minor displacements were critical for the rabbit. It seems that rabbits learn the location of things quite firmly and rely very little on vision or sound to locate objects that should be familiar to them, although sound (of a feeder, for example) seems to be a better cue than sight.

One of our most interesting observations concerning rabbits has to do with their behavior when the schedule of reinforcement calls for a very high ratio of responses to reinforcements. If, for example, a rabbit is required to depress a lever, or otherwise close a switch that fires a feeder, and we then put him on a fixed ratio requiring, say, six lever presses for each pellet of food, after fairly long experience with a schedule of this sort, we typically observe something like this: the rabbit will run off his six lever presses and the feeder will fire. However, instead of returning to the feeder, the rabbit will continue to press the lever and work through another fixed ratio series. He may do this three or four times before he finally returns to the feeder to get his food.

When this first occurred, we thought that the rabbit was simply "getting smart on us" and was merely piling up the food so that he wouldn't have to make more than one trip to collect it. Consequently, we put a bypass on the feeder which left the rabbit only the same number of pellets regardless of how many fixed ratio cycles he went through. However, the rabbit continued to run through several cycles in spite of the fact that he received no more food.

Although we are not certain of all the variables that account for this odd sort of behavior, we feel that part of the explanation lies in the way in which the rabbit normally makes a living. The rabbit is a herbivore; he customarily digs, scratches, and pulls to obtain roots and shoots and his other common food. For each small cycle of behavior, such as a dig or a tug, he is not accustomed to getting a large amount of food at one time, nor does he get a large energy input from the bite or the nibble that he succeeds in getting by, say, digging out a root, as compared to an equal volume of food value contained in a piece of meat that a carnivore obtains. Thus, it is relatively easy to get a rabbit to put out several subcycles, such as scratches or gnaws or nibbles, for a small amount of food because this is their customary practice. Furthermore, even though the rabbit may hear the feeder fire and "know" that the food is there, unlike the carnivore, he does not have to worry that his food will run away from him. If a cat does not latch onto a mouse right away, it is just too bad—the mouse may have gone. A rabbit is not in this unfortunate predicament.

HERBIVORES: THE UNGULATES

We have noted similar characteristics in cattle. If a cow is reinforced at an automatic feeder and then required to move, say, some six feet away from the feeder in order to pull a rope to work the feeder, she will exhibit very slight interest in turning to the feeder when it sounds. There will be much nuzzling, licking, and chewing on the rope before she finally ambles—slowly—to the feeder. What is more, this nonchalance about returning to the feeder after it has fired does not disappear if the cow becomes extremely hungry. She will not be much more apt to race to the feeder. Generally speaking, the cow is going to get to the feeder at her own bovine pace, regardless of how hungry she is. About the only way to get a cow to hurry is to frighten it or punish it.

It seems typical of these animals, as with the rabbits, who feed on low-energy packets, that their nature must be more tightly geared to the protective aspect of their behavior. In essence, evolution has forced them to make the choice between being food or getting food. A grazing animal typically does not get very much food at any one time nor for any one small cycle of behavior (in contrast to the carnivores, for example, who can sometimes procure several days' supply of food at one lunge). So we do not get markedly increased vigor or behavior with severely increased hunger drive (Grossman, 1965). We do get vigorous behavior when the escape behavior patterns are aroused.

We lost a considerable sum of money at one time by not realizing this—another of the incidents in our careers that led us to go back and take a closer look at the basic nature of animals. We might call this episode "The $8,000 Rump Roast." Our problems began when we wrote a script for a stage show featuring a cow without knowing very much about the nature of bovinity. According to the script, the cow was the companion of a lost miner. The script required the cow to perpetrate various outrages on the poor old miner—kick over his bucket, chase him around the campfire, knock down his tent, and finally stage a wild bull fight with him. It was a hilarious script, and we put a considerable amount of money into developing and selling this show before we had even trained the cows. However, when we started into the production of the behavior, interesting but painful problems began to develop. Aside from the matter of kicking the bucket, which we could not condition with food reinforcement at all (hence the name of the episode—it seems impossible to condition the rear end of a cow with food reinforcement), we were able to condition all the required behavior in the cow. The cow would chase the miner, knock down the tent, and engage in a bull fight—but all in lugubrious slow motion no matter how hungry she became. The whole slowed-down performance looked quite ridiculous. Needless to say, from there on we were quite careful about what kind of scripts we wrote for cattle.

The goat is a somewhat livelier character than the cow but shares certain of the same characteristics. As we have mentioned earlier (page 39), both goats and sheep imprint to people. If a kid or lamb is taken away from the mother at a very early age and raised on a bottle by a human being, it will attach very readily to the human and thereafter will not be very interested in goat or sheep companionship. This can be of great value to the experimenter, because goats and sheep who have been raised with others of their kind may be very reluctant experimental animals unless another animal is in the room with them. Liddell found this to be true in his early experiments with sheep (Liddell, 1950; Patton, 1951). Thus, an imprinted animal is a better one to work with, unless, of course, you are studying such a subject as social behavior in the normal flock.

Although we have no quantitative evidence on the matter, it seems that imprinting in the sheep is a much more sudden and irreversible process than in the case of the goat. The sheep in the first few days of life accepts either the mother or the human foster parent, and the attachment is virtually irreversible. Goats, apparently, do not need to be taken from the parents at such an early age, and even after being raised with humans, they will associate more readily with other goats even though this association does not seem to be essential to them, and they seem to prefer human companionship when it is available.

We have discovered that goats are extremely slow to form auditory discriminations. One problem presented to a goat was to learn to butt a rubber ball when a buzzer was sounding and not to butt it when the buzzer was off. This discrimination was finally established in several different goats, but only after between 800 to 1,200 trials as opposed to the very rapid conditioning of auditory discrimination in cats. This difference makes good sense when one considers the food-getting behaviors typical of the different species. Sounds make a difference in the hunting of the cat—it is important to listen for a rustle in the grass, the squeak of an animal. To a goat, sounds have little or nothing to do with feeding.

Conditioning of vocalizations for food reinforcements has always been a problem, and the question is by no means settled. At one time, we attempted to condition some goats to bleat for food. The plan was to have a goat do all the things a trick dog usually does

—speak, sit up, jump hurdles. "Speaking" proved to be formidably difficult: the goat simply did not bleat in the food-getting situation. We decided to try to elicit the bleat by other means and reward it with food. So we set up a situation with a triple push button. One button sounded a buzzer, the other gave the goat a mild shock, and the third worked the feeder. The plan was as follows: buzz, shock, wait for the bleat, then reinforce the goat with food. What happened was that after about 80 trials, the buzzer and the shock together would elicit both a jump and a bleat, but no number of pairings succeeded in conditioning the bleat. When the shock was dropped out, the buzzer elicited the jump but not the bleat. Preliminary study of when the animal in question usually vocalized might have helped here. Naturally the goat in his native state does not bleat for food. He may bleat for his mother and may bleat for the herd. In our experiments we did not try to reinforce the goat socially; this would have been an interesting experiment.

Rather more like goats than like cattle are the white-tailed and other similar deer. Delicate of limb and extremely agile, in the wild they can run at considerable speeds and execute some jumps of startling heights. The tiny fawn's principal protective device when its mother leaves it by itself is to sit quietly in a sheltered spot where its protective coloration effectively hides it from the eyes of most predators. The fawn's instinctive behavior patterns lead it to freeze rather than to run, so it can easily be picked up and carried home. Many a hunter has brought home a fawn found under such circumstances. Such a fawn raised by humans becomes extremely tame, like the cosset lamb, virtually imprinted to humans. They also become accustomed to the sight and sounds of dogs and so do not startle away from them; thus a deer so imprinted should never again be returned to the wild, because it would prove easy prey for hunters and dogs.

However, it seems that the startle pattern has not really been eliminated in these wild deer as it has in the domesticated ungulates. In man's true domestic animals much of the domestication process has consisted of breeding out the extreme startle patterns (as well as the extreme aggressions). In the deer, of course, there has been no opportunity for this selective breeding to have taken place. In fact, the selection has been all in the other direction. As the semidomesticated fawn matures, the tendency to freeze when danger threatens disappears, and gradually the fawn becomes more and more likely to startle and to run. Such an animal, if frightened, is apt to injure itself when confined to a fenced or other area, where it can run into things which in its normal life pattern would not be present. Apparently no amount of human association will eliminate this tendency of the truly wild animal to startle. Only a program of selective breeding can accomplish this.

Fawns have often been raised in this fashion for deer parks and zoos and provide considerable entertainment for the public when they are young. Even when grown, they continue to be extremely attached to humans and to seem quite tame. However, there is a true hazard as the male deer approaches maturity, which many zoo keepers and amateur deer handlers do not appreciate: the male deer during the mating season is an extremely dangerous animal, and may without any warning whatsoever turn upon and kill his keeper. In the male deer at this time the fighting pattern—ramming and butting with head and horns—will become unusually strong. The handler, unless he is aware of what is going on, finds himself in an extremely dangerous position. The deer will turn his head and seem to rub his head up against the handler, who thinks the deer is mighty sweet and is asking to be petted. However, what is happening is that the deer is getting his horns in position to ram, and if he is not careful, the handler may find himself with a sharp pronged horn piercing the soft part of his unprotected stomach. Again, this is essentially a failure of the domestication process. These aggressive tendencies have not been bred out, and at certain times of the year the powerful instincts connected with mating behavior sequences are simply too strong for the deer to resist, even though it has been brought up by the human. The soft parts of the man, stomach and unprotected chest and abdomen, match too well the acceptor pattern that the male deer has for the soft parts of a natural rival. There is no real bond of affection between the deer and the human, as the human might think would be the case. The deer reacts to the human at this stage as he would to a rival deer.

The horse is an interesting case of a partially domesticated animal. In the case of some of the older work breeds, the startle pattern has been quite effectively bred out for many generations. This, plus the weight and ponderousness of such draft horses, means that they are fairly steady, plodding animals. However, in the more volatile breeds, such as the race horse, the Arabian, and even the cow pony and American saddle horse, there has been little attempt to eliminate the swiftness with which such an animal will take off and run. These horses are still, for many purposes and in spite of their relationship with man, wild animals. The swiftness with which they will essentially startle and run contributes to their tremendous speed, and hence their usefulness to man in this case.

This brings up the interesting question of what is the relationship of man to the domesticated or semidomesticated horse, and the clues are revealed in the manner in which the horse is brought under control in practical situations. The process known as "breaking" is almost universally used as a method of getting the horse under control, and in fact, it seems to be virtually the only practical solution, although it is done more gently in some cases than in others, and is sometimes facilitated by a more positive approach. However, essentially, man does enforce his will on the horse, a process of "horsing." The horse is forcibly hauled around, "hazed," and sometimes quite brutally beaten and physically forced into control, keeping a saddle on his back, carrying a man, having his head jerked around to control direction and his flanks gouged to increase speed. Because the horse is a large and powerful animal, it is interesting that the horse allows this to happen at all. Why should he accept such treatment from a man? And after the man has successfully established himself as the master of the horse, why does he continue to be so placid and docile for such very small flicks of the whip?

Here again the answer lies in the herd life of the horse and the way in which he makes a living in the wild. The method of control used by the herd leaders of the wild herds gives us some of the clue here. The dominant animals in the herd control the herd by a process of "hazing" and "nipping," and it has been of selective advantage to the horse to yield to very slight cues. The horse's tendency in general to respond to almost subliminal stimuli has provided some famous cases in the history of animal psychology, the most notable of which was the nineteenth-century case of Clever Hans. Clever Hans was a European horse who performed miraculous feats, such as counting, "mind reading," and so on. After considerable investigation on the part of animal psychologists, it was discovered that Clever Hans was responding to unobtrusive hand and body movements made by his trainer, who did not even know that he was cuing the horse. This is the type of cue given by the trainers of trick horse acts seen at circuses and the like where the animal seems to be able to read, count, or pick out certain articles. Very slight shifts of body position, minute hand, head, or foot movements are being given by the trainer, again often without the trainer's awareness that he is so cuing the horse. This sensitivity to subtle cues is of considerable importance to the horse, who lives on the exposed open prairies and whose vision must be extremely ready to pick up the least signs of movements that may warn of predation and also to notice subtle signals from the leaders of the herd who may be in a position to guide him to safety.

CARNIVOROUS SPECIES: DOLPHINS

The carnivores, most of whom get their food by preying on other living animals (although a few of them consume dead protein), can be expected to exhibit some rather different behavioral properties, and indeed they do—many of them quite dramatically. However, before we consider the more typical carnivores, such as the cat and the dog, there are some interesting examples of what might be called transitional stages, certain animals who trace their ancestry to herbivorous species and who still exhibit some of the same characteristics of the herbivores even though they are at present predators.

One of the most interesting cases, at least in view of the current tremendous popular interest, is the dolphin, or porpoise. (The word *porpoise* is now being rather loosely used to cover the dolphins as well as the open ocean porpoises. *Porpoise* here will refer to both unless we specifically designate the bottle-nosed dolphin.) The bottle-nosed dolphin, *Tursiops truncatus,* very often popularly called a porpoise, is the common species exhibited at most aquaria. The bottle-nosed dolphin belongs to the Class Mammalia and to the Order Cetacea along with the whales and the other porpoises. He is, in fact, a small, toothed whale (as opposed to the toothless or baleen whales, which strain their food through the baleen or whalebone in their enormous mouths). Most experts on cetaceans now agree that dolphins and whales are descendants of a probably herbivorous creature that was also ancestral to the modern herbivorous ungulates (Slijper, 1958, pages 62–63), although there may be two fairly distinct lines of evolution that separated long ago. Also all but one of the large whales (the sperm whale is an exception), unlike their smaller relatives, are essentially grazers of the sea, because they feed on large diffuse masses of small vegetable and animal organisms of many kinds, krill (schools of tiny shrimp), small fish, snails, and occasionally even diatoms.

Often behavorial properties are an indication of evolutionary origin, and it is not surprising in view of the ancestry of the cetaceans that we can still see in their behavioral characteristics many of the properties of their common ancestry with the ungulates. Among these common behavioral properties may be the polyphasic sleep pattern—dolphins, like cows, do not take a long sleep, but get what they need in short catnaps (Alpers, 1960, page 85). One humorous trait that the bottle-nosed dolphins share with cows is their common exhibition of wary curiosity. Most farmers have noticed that if they throw an old glove or anything new on a fence line, very shortly the whole herd of cows will be up cautiously looking it over. Any new object in the pasture invites the same sort of wary inspection. The whole herd will stand around carefully staring at it, gradually coming closer to perhaps sniff and even lick. Porpoise trainers have noticed the same thing. Any new object in or near the tank evokes the same kind of wary curiosity, grave inspection, and cautious stand-offishness.

One of the most significant unusual traits that the porpoise shares with the cows in terms of training potential concerns the relation between food deprivation and vigor or intensity of behavior. It has been repeatedly observed at such aquaria as Marineland of Florida and Marineland of the Pacific, where extremely vigorous or intense behavior is sometimes required of the porpoise—such as in the 16-foot-high jump out of the water—that marked increases in food deprivation do not markedly increase the vigor or intensity of the response. Within limits, the porpoise is just as apt to jump 16 feet when he is not very hungry as when he is tremendously hungry.

We have already noted that it is extremely difficult to get fast or vigorous behavior from a cow with increased food deprivation, whereas, as we note elsewhere, other species such as the cat react quite differently under these conditions.

Also of importance to training is the fact that porpoises tend to be gentle, docile, and friendly, like many of the ungulates. They are quite unlike the sea lions in this respect. Generally speaking, the trainer does not have to worry about being bitten or otherwise attacked. Compared with other mature wild animals in captivity, porpoises rarely bite except in sexual encounters or in disciplining the young. They use a butting or ramming action in ordinary fighting. These behaviors are similar to the sexual biting of the horse and the fighting behavior of butting and ramming in cattle, goats, and sheep. Pilot whales, prior to mating, sometimes butt each other with their heads, and this, in a general way, reminds one of the cattle family, where the cows in heat often exhibit some of the behaviors of the bull. It is possible that the female pilot whale in heat also retains some of the behaviors of the male.

One fascinating problem of delphinology also may be related to their remote ancestry. There is no generally accepted theory about why dolphins and whales occasionally beach themselves and die in large numbers on the shores. However, we have evolved an interesting theory that has received support from some cetacean biologists which relates to their evolutionary ancestry and their common ancestry with the ungulates. There have been various theories advanced, such as failure of the animal's sonar system to warn them of the impending shore, and so on. However, these observations do not account for the fact that when the animals are towed back out to sea and released—even solitary animals—they return to the shore and again beach themselves (Layne, 1965). For example, on one occasion a lone pigmy sperm whale kept rebeaching itself even when shoved off the sands by a bulldozer.

Our theory relates to the observation that often these beachings occur in conditions of stress—storms, illness among the animals, and so on. As we have previously observed, in conditions of extreme stress, animals regress to more primitive behavior patterns. What this theory of cetacean beachings says then, is that in these conditions of stress, behavior patterns appropriate to their ancient evolutionary condition reappear.

In the course of cetacean evolution there was a time when the animals were gradually venturing farther and farther out into the water. At first they were basically land animals and stayed very close to the shore. At any threat of predation from sharks and other sea dangers, they would head for the shore, where they could not be pursued. Now in the open ocean this behavior pattern reappears in times of extreme stress, and the animals are driven onto the beaches regardless of the fact that the behavior pattern is no longer appropriate to their present totally aquatic circumstances. These tendencies also have a weird echo in the land ungulates' tendency to "spook"; the uncontrollable beachings of cetaceans may be similar in their origin and their results to the mad stampedes of cattle across the plains, which often end in disaster for the entire herd. This theory is not necessarily incompatible with Dudok van Heel's (1962) theory that beachings are caused by the failure of the animals' sonar systems, because in stress-produced regressions we can expect breakdowns of stimulus control. It should be noted, of course, that such hereditary tendencies as this are in the cetaceans' present milieu unadaptive and in fact, lethal. However, it seems that in other species these echoes do persist—the "spooking" we have noted, the flight of the lemmings to the sea, the overhuddling of some birds, the tendency, under stress, to destroy the young, and so on.

Probably one of the most discussed subjects in popular literature these days is the question of communication among the cetaceans, particularly the bottle-nosed dolphins. The extraordinary capabilities of the sonar system of *Tursiops truncatus* have been well documented (Kellogg, 1961), and since that time, extensive research has been done in a variety of laboratories concerning the use of their acoustic systems in interdolphin communication, object identification, and the like. The subject has received so much publicity and so much popular comment, and so many fanciful tales have been spun around it, that it is a very difficult one to treat rationally at this point. There is certainly no doubt that the porpoises do communicate with each other. However, whether the level and complexity of their communication represent anything different from the communications between other social animals is certainly a question that needs further considerable investigation.

Also the possibility of communication from dolphin to human and human to dolphin is something that is far from being settled in a laboratory. The "vocal" utterances of the dolphin are subject to modification with food reinforcement. Dolphins have been trained to emit sounds of a certain character, and there is some indication that these sounds can be shaped to resemble human speech. However, the question of the significance of this in terms of what the animal is really doing is far from being settled, and there is no conclusive experimental evidence at the present time to indicate that porpoises can communicate at anything like the conceptual level of complexity of human speech, nor is there any indication, where porpoises are observed to imitate human speech sounds, that these sounds "mean" anything to the porpoise remotely like what they mean to the human being. Of course, the questions of concept and meaning are themselves fraught with ambiguities.

Related to this subject is the question of the much-touted intelligence of the bottle-nosed dolphin. Here again, the subject has received so much publicity and has been the subject of so many high-flown stories that it is difficult to be objective about it. The dolphin is certainly a remarkable animal, but in certain respects he is no more remarkable than some of the other animals with which we have worked, such as the pig, for example, and the dog. This brings up, of course, the whole question of animal intelligence. Under what circumstances do we call an animal intelligent? The subject is one that is clouded in confusion because of the great varieties of behavior and "intelligences" among animal species. In a certain sense, one can say that any animal is the most intelligent for the ecological niche in which he is making a living. If it were not so, he would not be there. Certain species may be intelligent in one sense and not in another. However, generally speaking, those who speak of intelligence in animals seem to refer most often to characteristics similar to those of human beings—how does the animal stack up in certain regards in comparison to intelligent humans? In considering the problem in this light, although there has been no objective testing, we can endeavor to comment on the dolphin's comparative abilities.

First, quick conditioning is not necessarily an indication of intelligence. "One-trial" learning can occur in chickens as well as men, apes, and dolphins. Although many psychologists have considered the ability to form discriminations as a mark of intelligence, this is not necessarily the case. Some of the more limited, restricted birds, such as the chicken, are extremely good discriminators, and of course, the purest discrimination of all occurs in some extremely rigid animals, where the discrimination is fixed and built into the animal from birth— a specific reaction pattern to specific stimuli—such as the robin's discrimination of fighting behavior to the red spots on the breast.

However, one of the primary characteristics of intelligent animals seems to be their ability to generalize. Their acceptor patterns are not fixed and rigid. A behavior sequence that emerges in one set of circumstances is apt to emerge in a similar but different set of circumstances. If the porpoise has been trained to toss a ring back to his trainer, even when we throw a ball in the water, he will go to it without any hesitancy. Also a porpoise conditioned to toss a basketball into a goal has no difficulty in tossing the ball into the trainer's hand as well, even though the goal may be nearby. In other words, the trainer can readily become the stimulus pattern in place of the goal. A less "intelligent" animal may require many exposures to the ball and a gradual transition from ring to ball before it will take over. Similarly, a pig trained to put toys into a toy hamper will just as readily pick up camera stands and even the photographer's arm if you don't watch him. This is quite different from the case of the chicken, for example, who is a poor generalizer. A chicken trained to pull a tan-colored loop will eye a white loop for some time with a reptilian stare before giving it a try.

This is not to say that intelligent animals cannot form discriminations, for indeed they do. Some of them are quite good at it, but readiness to form discriminations is not in and of itself an indication of intelligence. There have not been very many quantitative studies reported of discrimination formation in the porpoise. Kellogg, at the First International Cetacean Symposium held in Washington in 1963, reported some discrimination experiments that indicated a much larger number of trials to perfection than would be expected with an "intelligent" animal. Other experiments that have not been published, and the details of which cannot be published because of their connection with military research, have shown similar problems. The porpoise may take a great many trials before beginning to establish a discrimination. However, when the proper techniques are used, the animal is capable of forming a discrimination much faster than when ordinary "automatic" laboratory methods are employed.

It is important to realize first that the behavior of the porpoise is very "cheap." Activity comes readily and easily and at low cost in terms of risk and organismic commitment. (See below, on play behavior.) And secondly, the porpoise is readily capable of forming fairly long sequences of behaviors. What this means is that if the porpoise is being required, say, to go to a pedal when a light is being flashed and ignore the pedal in the dark, it is extremely easy for the porpoise to make the wrong response, shift over quickly to the right response, and be reinforced. A few experiences like this will simply result in "pushing the pedal in the dark," being followed by "pushing the pedal in the light," followed by a piece of fish, and the porpoise has the whole thing neatly chained together—no apparent discrimination but simply a nice sequence of behavior. Because the porpoise "behaves" all the time—he swims vigorously and puts out a lot of energy in simply "fooling around"—pushing the pedal doesn't mean very much to him in terms of physical output. So he will with apparent good cheer go on pushing the wrong pedal for a long time, even though he is not rewarded. The slight delay that occurs when he makes a wrong response, and then a right response, and then is rewarded means little or nothing to him. He seems quite happy to do it that way if that is the way the experiment is set up.

In short, in designing discriminations for experiments for porpoises and other quick-moving "cheap behavior" animals, it is important in the first place to make the behavior sufficiently difficult so that it "means something" to the animal. Once the porpoise has made the choice between the right and wrong response, it should then be of some consequence to him if he has made a mistake. One possibility, for example, would be to move the choice point and the discriminative stimuli back and make the porpoise swim a fair distance after he has made a choice to get his fish. Another possibility is to put in a "time out" or a penalty time delay after he has made a mistake: after the animal has made a mistake, he should not be given a chance immediately to go and make the right response and be reinforced. This can be done by removing the manipulandum or turning off all signals. Also in quick establishment of a discrimination, a period of extinction conditioning on the "wrong" response is useful. In other words, all the positive stimuli should be cut off and let the animal simply repeat the response in the presence of the wrong stimuli until he is thoroughly extinguished.

Another indication of intelligence, another way in which "intelligent" animals are like human beings, is the ability to use behavior patterns that naturally fall under one "drive system" in the interest of another drive system. For example, in such animals a response pattern that normally would appear in fear or avoidance situations may be utilized in the food acquisition situation, and vice versa. Also a behavior pattern that is normally associated with sexual activity can be utilized to obtain food. In this respect the cetaceans measure up very well indeed. In fact, we have found this to be one of their most striking characteristics; namely, that almost any combination of muscular patterns can be conditioned. If the behavior can be elicited, or if the porpoise emits it in the presence of the trainer, it can be brought under control. This includes such conditioning as waving the flippers independently of each other, waving them simultaneously, conditioning the head movements in a vast variety of combinations in an exquisite degree of control, conditioning the tail to toss objects, tossing an object first with the tail, then immediately in sequence using the nose or the flipper to toss the same object, vocalization, including shaping of vocalizations in different pitches and intensities, squirting water, snorting with the blow-hole, rolling over, maintaining an upside-down position, and so on, literally, it appears, *ad infinitum*. Typical sexual behavior patterns in both female and male *Tursiops* have been brought under control with food reinforcement. This variety of behavior and this demonstration of "cross-drive conditioning" are features that are almost unheard of among the more restricted lower animals, and until we know more about the dolphins' communication abilities, these indications are perhaps the surest classifiers of the species in the category of the highly intelligent—the surest keys of entry into the ranks of the intellectuals of the animal world.

It is easy to see, both in dolphins and in man, that this great ease of conditioning and variety of behavior patterns are examples of what occurs in the neotenizing process. In a sense they are an index of indeterminacy or lack of crystallization. The process of neoteny, which we mentioned earlier as being perhaps built into the vertebrate evolution from the very beginning, in its simplest form means, you will recall, the arrival at reproductive maturity without maturation in many other respects. This process will produce an organism in its adult stage, some of whose fixed motor patterns or instincts have not gone to completion and hence will not be highly internally determined, crystallized, or built-in. Thus, there will be in his behavior system many possibilities for combination and recombination, both within the sequences of muscular contractions themselves and in coupling these with environmental inputs or stimuli. So we wind up with an animal that can do all sorts of things in a great variety of circumstances and whose behavior in a given circumstance is not rigid or stereotyped.

Another characteristic that dolphins share with many of the higher animals relates both to their neotenized condition and to their intelligence—namely, their playfulness. Like humans and other primates they have been known to invent quite fantastically complex "games" presumably for their own amusement, and certainly they have added to the enjoyment of the humans who have observed them (Hill, 1956). Their playfulness is partly a function of the favorable ecological niche in which the cetaceans find themselves, because, generally speaking, playful behavior is characteristic only of those species on whom predatory pressures are not great and who do not have to consume all their available energy in food gathering and staying alive. Conservation of energy comes easily to them. Of course, it is often the highly intelligent, successful animals who find themselves in this position. However, playfulness also is often a characteristic of immature and hence of neotenized organisms, particularly of the higher animals. It is interrelated with so-called intelligent behavior in many ways. For example, playfulness is another quality that makes possible the easy connectability of behavior patterns and the easy elicitation of a great variety of behavior patterns in a training or conditioning situation. It also has a great deal to do with general exploration and "preknowledge" of situations with perceptual and behavioral extensions that may come in handy later, in who knows what context.

So much for the friendly dolphin. A great deal more could be said, because he is such an absorbing topic of conversation. Before going on to consider the more typical carnivores, it might be well to say something about some of the other relatives of the dolphin. The great baleen whales (of the Suborder *Mystacocetes*) have been the subject of very little behavioral investigation, and open-ocean observations have been confined largely to the economically worthwhile investigation of such topics as migration routes and population trends. However, pilot whales (small-toothed whales not too distant from the dolphins in their ancestry but considerably larger) have been introduced into the aquaria in this country in recent years. In fact, we happened to be on hand at the time the first one was captured and brought successfully into the Marineland of California Oceanarium. They are not too different from the dolphin in many of their behavioral characteristics. Their movements are slower and more ponderous, and they are also inclined to be somewhat less emotional. In general, they seem to be just a slowed-down, more bovine version of the dolphin. Aside from their rather cumbersome movements, they can apparently learn just as much and just as readily as the dolphin; the observations we have made about intelligence and variety of behavior, cross-drive conditioning, and so on, apparently apply equally well to them.

When we come to a more typical land carnivore, we come to quite a different type of animal.

CARNIVORES: CATS AND DOGS

The felines are the ultimate carnivores, you might say. They are almost universally solitary animals, hunters of live prey, and extremely rugged, bad-tempered individuals. In the wild, cats live almost completely alone except during the mating season and, of course, during their infancy, when they may be raised with one or more litter mates. As a result of this, they have not developed any sort of elaborate social patterns among themselves. One outstanding exception to this is the African lion, who has developed loose associations known as "prides"; in this case, it is interesting to note that the lion, unlike the other cats, shows signs of sexual dimorphism (the tendency of the sexes to show different physical forms or traits), the male being larger than the female and sporting the well-known prominent mane. Such dimorphism often appears in group-living animals.

Cats in the wild do not chase or course their prey as do the dogs and some other animals. Consequently, their attempts to get food are characterized by sudden outbursts of energy for a very short period of time. Typically, they lie and wait, make an extremely short, intense rush and pounce. If they miss, they do not pursue for any length but simply wait for another chance at another time. This means that at all times their attention must be glued to the object of their attack; because the cats hunt primarily by visual means, even at night, they focus their eyes very sharply on the source of their food, in this case, their prey.

In a laboratory learning situation or in a home pet-training situation, it is easy to see vividly the effects of these behavioral characteristics. In any learning situation where food is the reward, their attention will be almost completely absorbed by the source of the food itself. If it is in the trainer's hand, the cat watches the hand. If it is in any sort of a container, the cat's attention is riveted on the container, as we have noted above (page 64). In any situation it is very difficult to get the cat away from the source of the food to do something in order to activate the source.

Also, because the cat does not course his game, his persistence for food at any one time is not too long-lived. If we require the cat to make a response requiring a larger outlay of energy, he will go through one sequence but then may very well lie down and go to sleep if he doesn't achieve success in the first trial. However, simpler sequences of behavior requiring less energy are somewhat different. The cat will, in such cases, take a ratio rather well, emitting large numbers of responses fairly consistently in order to get his reward. As a result of all these characteristics, cats have usually done well in problem-solving situations in laboratories where the cat is put into isolation and given some problem to solve by himself, particularly where he does not have to go far away from the source of the food in order to go through behavioral sequences to get the food. Grossman (1965) has noted the tendency of certain kinds of apparatus, such as the Skinner box, to force all organisms into a sort of behavioral conformity.

Another infuriating characteristic of the cat's behavior not only results in many stepped-upon tails but also makes it difficult to train in situations where a human being is present. This we might call "importuning" behavior. Probably every cat owner has observed it at feeding time. When a cat is hungry and food seems imminent, a very strong instinctive pattern appears. There will be a great deal of rubbing up against the refrigerator and most particularly against the legs of the owner. If the owner isn't careful, he will find himself tripped up, and if the cat isn't careful, he will find himself being stepped on. However, no amount of being stepped on seems to discourage the cat from this sort of behavior. The appearance of this very strong behavior can radically interfere with the training situation. And so it is that in an ordinary home-training situation with the owner present, the cats generally do very poorly, and there is very little cat training accomplished.

The nature of this importuning behavior in the cat is interesting in light of what we have said before concerning the neotenizing process in the vertebrates. During the thousands of years of domestication of the cat (which has not occupied anywhere near as many years as that of the dog) much of the selective breeding was, no doubt, designed to breed out the extreme wildness and aggressiveness of the truly wild cat. In the process of breeding out this aggressiveness, there was also bred into the domestic cat the tendency to be babyish and infantile in other regards. The importuning behavior is part of the grown domestic cat's persistent kittenish behavior. When the mother cat comes home from hunting, the kittens rub up against the mother's legs, probably in an attempt to get the mother to lie down and nurse; at least this is what generally happens.

Adult domestic cats can also, of course, live together amicably in large groups even though they are not herd or group animals in the wild. Again, this is a reflection of the infantile state. In other words, a group of grown cats gets along because a litter of kittens get along. They never reach the point where they are jealous or fight among themselves as much as they would if they were not neotenized.

Thus although the cat seems thoroughly independent as compared to the dog, its behavior is somewhat social in this regard and also in its relationship with humans. The cat reacts to the human as it would to its mother, and here again we see neoteny at work. To the cat, patting and rubbing by the human is similar to being licked and groomed by the mother cat. Kittens, as we have seen, are at least temporarily social creatures, even the kittens of the wild cats, and some concern for or interest in the presence of other creatures can be interpreted as a result of the preservation of this kittenish state. Another obvious characteristic, too, which comes with neotenization, as we mentioned in connection with dolphins, is playfulness. Certainly grown domestic cats are much more playful than grown wild cats.

In any discussion of the cat, one of the most heated subjects of conversation is the dog. How are dogs different from cats? Are they smarter than cats, better than cats, and so on? Few subjects can arouse such violent arguments even though dogs and cats often share the same household. In the United States alone, 26 million dogs vie with 28 million cats for the affection of pet owners (according to Edwin E. Rosenblum, editor of *All Pets* magazine, in personal communication).

One perfectly obvious point is that dogs are quite different from cats. Unlike cats, dogs are, in the wild, pack animals and have developed over the millions of years their extensive social patterns to prevent in-group fighting and encourage cooperation for the common good. Usually, there is some sort of status hierarchy within the pack or the group as there is in the case of most social animals —for example, the pecking order in chickens. Thus, there is one very strong leader to whom all the rest of the animals are more or less submissive, and a regular social hierarchy existing among the lesser ones. In the dog pack, there is a top dog or a master wolf who keeps peace among the other animals, who are strictly subservient to him.

Along with this social hierarchy, the dogs have developed elaborate signal systems by which they indicate their emotional state to the others—ear and tail signals to indicate readiness to fight or to submit, to signal the others to a group effort, and the like. Thus, as a result there is actually very little fighting among a pack of wolves.

Most of it is bluffing and threatening. When man domesticated the dog and bred him to transfer his allegiance and affections to a human being, man was able to capitalize on all of this built-in social behavior.

The cat, on the other hand, does not have this in its evolutionary background and so has some strikingly different characteristics in its relationships to human beings. In this regard, the cat is truly independent. It does not have to depend on social acceptance in the group, and it is not threatened by any sort of a minor social situation that can be quite disturbing to a dog. When we threaten a dog with scolding or shouts or punishment, we plug into its natural tendency to avoid the "dressing down" by the top dog of the pack. A cat, which is not worried by any such superior persons in its native group, is not the least bit worried about scolding and is notoriously impervious to punishment. The cat is quite a tough creature and in infantile play is extremely rough. It does not mind being scratched and batted about rather vigorously. All this results in what you might call a very weak superego in the cat. Its instinctive "code of ethics" does not call for being sorry for what it has done in the past.

So we find that the cat in its relationships with human beings does not have the great dependency on affection that dogs have. The cat does not perform for or do the will of the owner as a dog will simply for a pat on the head or a kind word. The cat is not so apt to follow the owner through the fields or away from the house or go with him in the car. We have noted that the relationship of the human to the domestic cat is more that of the mother to the kitten. In the case of the dog, however, although the dog is also a considerably neotenized animal, something different seems to have happened, and the dog has taken the man as the pack leader rather than as a parent, although there are still some traces of parental relationships, the puppyish crying of the injured dog, playfulness in the adult dog, and so on. Different breeds differ considerably in the extent to which they are neotenized. Some of the smaller toy and special breeds particularly are considerably neotenized; for example, a German shepherd is a pretty rugged, independent individual as compared to a chihuahua, and many poodles seem to represent extremes of puppyish dependency.

The dog and the cat are the only two truly domesticated carnivores in man's life. If you have watched barnyard cats making their living and shying away from human contact and have perhaps had your hands clawed by male Siamese in fits of pique, you may sometimes wonder how domesticated the cat is. However, as we have seen, they are far, far gentler and more amenable to the society of man than their close relatives—the small wildcats, such as the bobcat and the lynx. The dog, too, has been called the wolf in the house and preserves many of the characteristics of his wild brothers, including interbreeding with them. In some of the fiercer, more independent breeds, such as the husky and the German shepherd, it is indeed hard to distinguish wolf from domestic dog. However, domestic dogs and cats are truly docile, domesticated animals as compared to some of the wild carnivores that man has raised as pets—lions, leopards, ocelots, cheetahs, and such exotic species as otters and sea lions. These animals remain basically wild animals who can never truly be trusted. They may turn on their human friends without warning, rending and even killing them. Although the playful sea lion is a source of vast amusement in zoos and circuses and may appear quite docile, gentle, and easy to handle, it is a rare sea lion trainer who doesn't bear tooth marks on his hands and arms, and the large wildcats such as the lions and tigers in the circus cages are not fooling. The big cats, interestingly enough, are not trained with the reward methods of modern neo-behavioristic psychology nor with the cruder fish-tossing techniques of the traditional sea lion trainer. The big cat act represents a delicate balancing of the cat's alternating tendencies to flee from the whips and cracking guns and to attack the trainer. It is not too uncommon for the trainer to be attacked when things get out of hand. It is a perilous and exacting business, and the big cat trainer is in deadly danger every moment he is in the cage with the animals. There is no love lost on the trainer on the part of the big cats.

OMNIVORES: RATS TO RACCOONS

Some of the most successful of all animals are those who like man will eat anything—the omnivores. Among the mammals, in addition to man and many of the monkeys, are raccoons, bears, rats, mice, and pigs. All of these are extremely successful animals in their own right. They are broad-niched, and can be found in many different circumstances. They make their living in many ways, and are not as dependent as the carnivores or the exclusive vegetarians on the availability of a certain kind of food. The ease with which some of them become true pests, such as rats, mice, and in certain localities, raccoons and bears, testifies to the success of their mode of living. It is not only in their omnivorous diet, however, that many of these animals are successful. Although we have mentioned some of the pitfalls involved in a discussion of animal intelligence, if animals are to be ranked according to some of the criteria we have been discussing, it would be obvious that the raccoon, bears, and pigs are all fairly well off on these scales. They are generalizers. For example, they can transfer learning readily from one situation to another—in fact, their generalizing ability may explain their omnivorous tendencies.

In addition to its generalizing ability, the raccoon has a great variety of behavior and possesses a manipulative ability almost equal to that of some of the monkeys. Raccoons have often been raised as pets and become quite engaging companions around the household, but like many of the wild carnivores, a raccoon so raised becomes a somewhat unreliable customer when he reaches sexual maturity. Again, the raccoon's busy hands and speed and agility enable him to become quite a pest around campsites, and like the bear, he is noted for his ability to raid garbage cans and tents. Although not as commonly seen in the role of performing animal as the bear, a raccoon can be taught quite a variety of entertaining behavior, such as playing basketball, playing the piano, doing various types of acrobatics, and the like.

The pig too is a good generalizer and a tremendous worker. With his large appetite for food, he will keep working at learning situations virtually unendingly.

It was the pig who first introduced us to the interesting philosophical question "What is the animal doing?" Part of a series of behaviors, which we were teaching a pig for a General Mills Farm Feed Show, involved picking articles up off the floor and depositing them in a hamper. This proved more difficult than we had anticipated. We started with an article next to and on the left of the hamper. With considerable difficulty, we trained the pig to pick up the article and to raise his head higher and higher until finally he reached the point where he could get it over the edge of the hamper and at last to drop it. But to turn the article loose proved more difficult than we had anticipated. Very often he would drag it back out with him and would have to start over again. (We later licked this problem by what now seems to us the obvious method—starting as near the end of the sequence as we could and working backward. That is, we now teach the pig to drop the article first, which is followed immediately by the eating chain, and so on back to picking up the article near the hamper.) However, because we wanted the pig to pick up articles over a wide area, after this first sequence was finally perfected, we put the article a scant few inches on the right side of the hamper. Now, to our dismay, instead of picking up the article and depositing it in the hamper, the pig picked up the article and moved off to the right in gyrating motions, tossing the article as he went and finally bumping into the wall on the far side. When we thought he was "putting the article in the hamper," he was actually doing no such thing. A more accurate description would be to say that with the article in his mouth, he was making circular movements to the right. If the hamper were in the right place, these would result in his colliding with the hamper and putting the article in it. So, we had to start over again, gradually moving the article around from the left side to the right side until we finally achieved it.

Not much needs to be said about rats and mice, because they are common objects of study in the laboratory. But it should be pointed out that many characteristics of these rodents are highly specialized. They are extremely good maze runners; it is probably fortunate that the maze was seized upon as an early device for studying their behavior because they naturally make their living in dark tunnels and burrows and the like. They are also nocturnal animals, and this fact should be remembered in considering studies involving light signals and light intensities. The rat is a dweller in deep darkness who makes a living by going out into dim but not bright light, as we noted in our section on the laboratory niche.

The hamster, although less known to American psychologists, is an interesting little animal in his own right, but he does have some problems as far as laboratory use is concerned. He is not as durable as the rat and is a semihibernator. He will roll up and turn cold on very slight provocation unless kept under extremely favorable temperature conditions. Because he pouches his food, he represents some interesting theoretical problems to the psychologist. In a food-getting situation where the hamster is given an opportunity to disgorge his food, he will work away, fill his pouches, and then disgorge. The experimenter can slyly steal the food, and the hamster will go on working perhaps indefinitely. This, so far as we know, has never been carried to its limits, but it would be an interesting experiment. Similarly, a hamster in a situation where he is not given an opportunity to disgorge becomes very nervous and will stop working for a long period of time, even though he is still hungry, running excitedly back and forth in an attempt to get out to his nest. Perhaps because of his manner of making a living on the steppes of Asia and not engaging in a running battle with man, as have the rat and the mouse, the hamster is tamer and somewhat easier to handle, not as prone to startling, and, of course, much slower-moving than the rat or the mouse.

OF, BY, AND FOR THE BIRDS

Before we go on to consider what is apparently the culmination of evolution in the mammalian world, we might digress briefly to discuss the birds. The birds branched off from ancestral reptilian stock at about the same time as the mammals but have since gone their own diverse and fascinating path. Although they are often considered as lower animals by human classifiers, they are an extremely diverse group in their own right and exhibit vast ranges of various abilities. There are both broad-niched and narrow-niched birds, adaptable birds and stereotyped birds, generalizers and specializers. They have evolved fascinating specialties, both physically and behaviorally, for getting along in the world.

Birds have been the serious subject of numerous investigations on the inheritance of behavior patterns, because many groups apparently come with rather highly specific behavior patterns already "wired in." For example, as we mentioned earlier, Dilger (1962) has shown in a fascinating study that when two closely related species of love birds, which have different nest-building patterns, are mated, the resulting offspring show a nest-building behavior that is a blend of that of the two parents—often a nonadaptive blend that results in great difficulties in nest construction. All in all, there is probably as great a variety among birds as there is among mammals in the characteristics that are of interest to students of behavior, both with regard to physical properties, "intelligence," and the like.

Many of the seed-eating birds are relatively narrow-niched and highly specialized. Their behavior is apt to be quite restricted and rather invariant. Many of them have developed remarkable specialties for dealing with the kind of seeds that make up their diet, and if these seeds were suddenly to be blown from the face of the earth, they would be in a bad way. Some of the passerine or perching birds seem to be somewhat more restricted than the others, but there are some remarkably broad-niched birds among the seed eaters. Pigeons (not passerines but belonging to the Order Columbiformes) are probably the most remarkable and pestiferous examples. Although apparently more or less strict vegetarians and primarily seed eaters, pigeons have succeeded remarkably in making a living among human habitations. They are remarkable birds in many ways—unique in their secretion of crop milk, with which they feed the young, their method of drinking (they can sip water up with their heads in a lowered position, unlike other birds, who must tip their heads back to swallow each mouthful), and their well-known and spectacular homing abilities. Of course, man as usual has tampered with the pigeon's genetics and bred many fancy breeds with various behavior traits, such as tumbling and pouting.

The pigeon has proved to be a remarkably suitable laboratory animal and is, in many laboratories, supplanting the rat as the animal of choice. The bird's keen vision and the tremendous reliability of the pecking response under a great variety of unusual laboratory conditions led to its use in the fascinating guided-missile project during the war (Skinner, 1960). In spite of their being tossed, turned, rotated, gyrated, drugged, and subjected to all manner of noises and distractions, the birds kept up an extraordinary volley of high-speed pecks at the target, thus producing a highly reliable system for guiding missiles. Unfortunately, at that time the military imagination was not quite able to grasp the significance of what had been done; furthermore, there were no guidable missiles at that time, so the project was dropped before it actually came to practical fruition.

The pecking response of the pigeon is primarily the one that has been used in laboratory studies. In fact, it is one of the limitations of this otherwise remarkable bird that aside from the peck, it has very little other behavior except gross bodily movements. Unlike some of the birds that feed on a more varied diet, it pecks rather than pulls, tugs, or scratches. At our laboratory, we had an extraordinarily difficult time getting the pigeon to pull a small loop—something that is virtually sure-fire in the first day of work with a chicken, for example. Only by a gradual transition from a peck and by essentially fooling the bird into pulling the string were we able to achieve what we wanted.

Like many of the other birds and the more restricted lower mammals, the pigeon is also restricted in his ability to condition across drive systems; that is to say, a type of behavior sequence that is tightly connected, say, with food-getting sequences will be emitted only with extreme difficulty, if at all, when other conditions in the bird are aroused. We have already commented (see pages 63) on the problem of getting a pigeon to peck a key to turn off a shock. Time and time again we have found problems like this in the lower, more restricted animals. This relative ease or difficulty of such cross-drive conditioning, as we have mentioned in the case of the dolphin, is perhaps one of the criteria we might apply to interspecies comparisons of intelligence.

Fowl, both water-fowl and the land species, such as chickens, turkeys, peafowl, and so on, are again different sorts of birds. Many of them are omnivores and will eat insects, small animals, seeds, grasses, and leaves. Many of the ducks, of course, are fish eaters as well as feeders on vegetable matter. The fowl are something special in the bird world in that their babies come prepared to make their way in the world on their hatching day, unlike the helpless nestlings of the passerines and some others who must spend a month or more in complete naked dependence upon their parents. A day-old baby chick, suitably dried off, fluffed up, and on his feet, will in very short order start to run around the barnyard, follow its mother, scratch, chase bugs, fight with its brothers and sisters, and so on. The behavior of infant chicks has received a great deal of attention in experimental literature (Kuo, 1932).

More recently, chicks, ducklings, and goslings have been the subject of extensive investigation by the ethologists with regard to the phenomenon of imprinting (see pages 38 and 39). The ramifications and elaborations of this process have recently filled many volumes of psychological literature. Considering the conditions under which the baby chick or duckling is hatched, its tendency to follow the first moving object it sees makes considerably good sense. (The irreversibility of the process differs with the different species and with the age of the animal.)

However, just as man has tampered with genetics of his domestic animals, so in the imprinting experiments he has tampered with the "wiring in" of irreversible behavior patterns when he imprints chicks and ducklings to moving balls, walking feet, toy cars, and the like. The imprinting process, apparently, has a broader significance for the animal, however, than simply the tendency to follow moving objects. We once raised a young duckling in a brooder with a group of baby chicks. When the chicks and the ducklings were almost grown, we put the duckling out in the yard in the pond with the other ducks, thinking he would be perfectly happy there. But he spent all of his time rattling up and down the fence, trying to get back into the pen with the chickens whom he could see over in the next yard. Finally, because the poor thing was wearing himself out, we put him in the yard with the chickens where he was quite content. When he reached maturity, however, he encountered more frustration, because instead of picking himself out a nice young duck for a mate (although both chickens and ducks were now together) he insisted on bestowing his attentions on a little hen. Because their respective behavior patterns failed to "jibe," nothing happened to consummate this unfortunate would-be union, and both drake and hen were completely exhausted after several weeks of unrelenting but unsuccessful attempts.

In a general attenuated sense, perhaps we can see the phenomenon of imprinting operating in the higher animals to help them identify the ones of their kind with whom they should mate. A young raccoon, raised on a bottle by human hands, when grown, was placed into a cage next to another raccoon and was terrified of the animal, having never seen anything like this before. Unnaturally imprinted animals often do not mate or raise their young successfully, as Harlow has discovered (see reading [5]). Note that this "natural imprinting" in the sense of ultimate mate selection can result from being raised with young of the same kind (as Harlow discovered and as occurs in the case of chicks and ducklings).

It is possible that perhaps even in the human case we can see effects of unnatural imprinting in "miscarriages" of the Oedipus and Electra complexes. The growing young man or woman certainly needs some guidance in what sort of person he should take as a mate. The most logical thing in the world is for him to use as his ideal and his model his mother or in the girl's case, her father. Sir Francis Galton demonstrated this effect of "imprinting" in his famous "Coefficient of Assortative Mating," which demonstrated the correlation in physical attributes between human mates. Although this correlation is far from perfect, apparently something like imprinting in the family situation results in the maturing boy's selecting a mate at least similar to his mother in many respects. The psychoanalytical findings concerning the Oedipus and Electra complexes, namely that when these stages are unsatisfactorily handled for one reason or another the grown person may never be capable of a successful marriage, are analogous to the results of attempted matings between unnaturally imprinted birds.

Improper imprinting also occurs in the wild. Over a period of time at a wilderness lake, we observed a solitary gray goose who was apparently imprinted to a flock of mud hens. Perhaps something had happened to his parents and brothers and sisters so that when he hatched he found himself all alone. He no doubt would not have survived at all had he not been able to attach himself to the first group of moving things he saw—in this case, a flock of mud hens. He spent all of his time with them and made no attempt to join other flocks of geese when they came and went on their migrations.

Both ducks and chickens have proved to be excellent laboratory animals. Chickens are perhaps a better specimen for an ordinary laboratory to use because of ease of maintenance. Ducks have some problems; to be kept in good physical condition, they need at least occasional access to bathing water; over long periods of time they need to be kept on a solid floor rather than on wire because of the sensitivity of their feet; also they are considerably messier than chickens. As far as behavior capabilities and general conditionability, ducks and chickens are similar, although we have observed that ducks are much more emotional than chickens. Unless the ducklings are taken when only a few days old from the society of other ducks and raised in isolation with a human "parent," they are apt to be highly wary, easily startled, and thus unsuited for many types of experimental work and particularly for public exhibition. For this reason, we have developed a standard practice of imprinting ducklings (and geese) to humans. We separate them, put them in small individual brooders, and raise them in close association with humans, usually asking schoolchildren to raise them for us and play with them daily. The result is a remarkably tame and successful experimental animal. If anyone is planning to study ducks in anything except natural wild conditions, we would certainly recommend this procedure.

It should be noted that imprinting of this sort, with Pekin ducklings at least, does not always result in failure to mate with their own kind later on. We have successfully mated imprinted ducks to imprinted drakes, but with some of the more primitive species of ducks or geese this might not work out so successfully.

The duck does not quite have such a variety of behavior patterns as the chicken because it is a somewhat more specialized animal. However, it can peck, in its fashion, it can pull and tug, and its swimming behavior can be brought under control, patterned, and shaped with food reinforcements.

Chickens are remarkably adaptable and useful laboratory animals, especially the heavy broiler breeds. The lighter weight, egg-laying breeds, such as the Leghorns and Minorcas, are not recommended for experimental work because of their high emotionality. We have also used, to a large extent, the ordinary small barnyard bantam—here again a heavy breed bantam is recommended. Some of these are almost as small as pigeons and thus take up less space and eat less than the larger breeds of hens. They are very tame and hardy creatures. Hens are more satisfactory than roosters, because the latter are apt, at crucial moments, to be more interested in fighting and showing off than in eating.

All chickens have more variety of behavior than the pigeon and, as we have just noted, more than the duck. They are omnivores—they eat seeds, leaves, garden plants, worms, bugs (and pursue their prey in these cases), garbage and, as a last resort, chicken feed. In the course of behaving they pull, tug, peck, and scratch. A great deal is known about them genetically because of the long breeding records that have been kept by hatcheries on special strains. Therefore, it is possible to get a very pure strain of fowl to use for genetic and behavioral studies.

There are many fascinating parallels between the life of various flocks of barnyard and wild fowl and human societies. Guhl in his address to the Kansas Academy of Science (1963) has pointed out the potential significance of many of these. The "pecking order" among fowl—the dominance relationships within a flock—has interesting parallels with the dominance relations in human societies. Also the phenomena of stress and overcrowding among flocks, inheritance of aggressiveness, and the problems of color and "race" discrimination may have interesting relevance to problems of human society.

Observations on the chicken were responsible for some of our earliest realizations that animal species were remarkably different in their behavioral tendencies, that not all behavioral sequences were equally conditionable, that some sequences come "wired in" to an animal in such a form as to be virtually ineradicable, and that one had better be mighty careful if he thinks he knows what he is saying when he describes a sequence of behavior. For example, we discovered that the chicken, unlike the pigeon, could very easily be taught to pull things because this was one of the very easiest things for the chicken to do. Presenting the chicken with a rubber loop or a string was just about like presenting it with an angle worm. In contrast with the days and weeks that are sometimes required to get a pigeon to pull a string, chickens can do it within five or ten minutes, and sometimes even a few seconds.

Also, we discovered that it was practically impossible for a chicken to do nothing; unlike the cat who can sit quietly and fixate on the source of the food for several minutes and the dog who can readily be taught to stay in one location, the chicken apparently cannot simply stand still in one spot for any length of time if this standing still is followed by the appearance of food. What happens is that throwing any sort of delay into a food-getting sequence almost invariably brings out the chicken's scratching pattern, a prominent part of the behavior with which the gallinaceous birds make their living in the wild. As we described in "The Misbehavior of Organisms" (Breland and Breland, 1961), whereas all the chicken needs to do is stand on the platform for a few seconds, the tendency of the scratch pattern to emerge is so strong that the chickens do not have to be specifically "trained" to scratch. The pattern generally comes out willy-nilly, and chickens have been known to make as many as 10,000 unnecessary responses in a day—if you consider each cycle of the typical foot-scratching movements as a response.

On the other hand, we found that it was virtually impossible to get the chicken to vocalize for food reinforcement. This has been done (Lane, 1961) with considerable difficulty by an experimenter who happened to pick up the small food-associated cluckings. However, in the case of usual vocalization of the chicken, when such a sequence is followed by food, it becomes weaker rather than stronger and gradually drops out altogether.

Some interesting problems have arisen in connection with the pecking sequences. It may appear that the chicken is pecking with a closed beak at an object, but photographic analysis will show that the chicken is actually pecking with open beak and the amount that the beak is open is virtually precisely the size of the dot or spot at which she is pecking. This leads to some interesting complications in the design of apparatus. For example: if a round object, say half an inch in diameter, is used for a manipulandum for the chicken to peck at, although the chicken may occasionally strike at this with almost closed beak and hit it a hard knock, the predominating tendency will be for her to grab the article and tug at it. If it is loose, she will pick it up, throw it up in the air, and crack it on the ground (for all the world like a chicken trying to crack open a seed pod). If the object is attached, she will bite it and pull at it. Apparently a fairly typical sequence in the chicken's wild hunting behavior is a sharp peck at a pod or bug and then a grab—the chicken will pick up the food article and toss it around, either killing it or cracking it open. These tendencies, too, have led to some interesting complications in our own work.

In our capsule-vending chicken exhibit (Breland and Breland,

1961), a chicken pulls a loop to release a capsule, containing a toy or souvenir, from a hopper above her head. The capsule slides down a chute, and the chicken is then required to give it a good vigorous straightforward peck and knock it out to the customer. However, in a large percentage of cases, the chicken is so entranced with the capsule, which often sparkles, rolls, and rattles, that she will pick it up in her beak and drag it back into the cage with her, slamming it onto the floor of the cage. This results in no reinforcement for the chicken and, of course, no capsule for the customer.

The persistence of this nonreinforced behavior is truly remarkable. As the chicken gets hungrier, the problem behavior gets worse. We were forced to fail such a large number—an average of 20 percent—of chickens because of this problem that we made a purely physical change. We reduced the size of the chicken—by using bantam hens. Their beaks were so small that they could not readily pick up the large capsules and drag them in, although some of them still managed to steal a few. Apparently, the rattling, rolling capsule fires off the grabbing, shaking sequence so strongly that the chicken is unable to overcome it, and it persists in spite of nonreinforcement.

The chicken on more than one occasion has proved highly educational with regard to the objective description of animal behavior. It was particularly interesting in light of the experiments reported by B. F. Skinner on head raising in the pigeon (Skinner, 1961, p. 48). As part of some of our demonstrations for show purposes, we had taught chickens to tip their heads back and had further exaggerated this into a weird twisting movement of the head. In one attempt to objectify the training instructions for this head lifting, we adopted Skinner's technique of making a graduated scale against the wall where we could see how high the chicken had actually lifted her head. The chicken was free on a table, and as a scale we used inch rulings marked off on a cardboard box. We then started reinforcing the chicken for lifting her head, checking the extent of the lift against the scale. The chicken stretched higher and higher. We watched the head movements and the neck very carefully all the time so that we could see precisely what the chicken was doing. Suddenly, to our consternation, the chicken wasn't there. She was on top of the box! In other words, we were not reinforcing necessarily head lifting, but the incipient movements of jumping up to a perch. Thus it seems that there are dangers in talking about "head lifting" in relation to a scale marked off against the wall.

The chicken, like most other birds, has extremely keen eyesight, and visual discriminations are very easy for fowl. A laboratory-adapted chicken can in the course of a session lasting a few minutes form discriminations between diamonds and squares, red and black dots, and other similar visual presentations. They can learn to pick a tiny dot in the midst of a large and diffused pattern. One little part of a miniature stage show called "the old shell game" requires the chicken unerringly to pick the walnut shell under which a pea is hidden, in spite of changes in position of the "hot" shell. The cue is a tiny natural pattern on the shell, and it is a difficult discrimination for human eyes.

This ability of the chicken to make visual discriminations reiterates the point that ability to make discriminations is not necessarily an indication of high intelligence of the human variety. Difficulties with dolphins, pigs, and other animals in forming discriminations do not necessarily indicate a lack of intelligence. One of the reasons a chicken finds it so easy to make discriminations is that it does not generalize. It has no tendencies to drift off the subject—the chicken sticks to the task at hand.

On the other hand, let us take a look at the psittacines—the parrots, macaws, cockatoos, love birds, and the like. These are the monkeys of the bird world. In contrast to some of the more specialized birds, these birds are extremely good generalizers. Although it is true that they are specialists themselves in certain regards—note, for example, their massive beaks, which they use for cracking seeds, chewing up trees, peoples' fingers, and the like—and although they are relatively narrow-niched in terms of the climate they can tolerate (they are highly tropical birds), they are extraordinary behavioral generalists. They have a great variety of behavior, they use both their beaks and their claws and can manipulate them in a great variety of ways—for example, they pick up straws and scratch their ears—they have a great deal of play behavior, and they can put behavior sequences together in a remarkable series of movements. They are capable of chaining out sequences and recombining their behaviors in ways that are quite impossible for more limited birds. For example, we have trained cockatoos to ride a counterweighted bicycle on a tight wire; here the cockatoos exceeded even our expectations. We thought with luck that we would be able to get the cockatoo to climb on the bicycle and sit there holding his feet on the pedals, letting the bicycle roll down the wire. And possibly, with a little more luck, we might get the cockatoo to push forward with one foot and then let his other foot coast around. However, much to our surprise, the cockatoo developed his own quite advanced way of doing this. He pushed with one foot and pulled with the other, just as a person would when working an exercise machine or double crank with his hands. The entire sequence, which terminates with one peanut, goes as follows: the cockatoo climbs the bicycle, grasps the handlebar with his beak and the foot pedals with his feet, pushes with one foot and pulls with the other, pedals along in perfectly human fashion to the end of the wire, gets off, and receives his peanut.

However, when it comes to forming visual discriminations, the cockatoos and macaws present more problems than chickens. Because they are generalizers, they are more apt to make mistakes in learning a discrimination. It takes a considerable amount of time and patience to teach a macaw to do the old shell game even with large shells and a big black spot. It is not that their vision is not good, but they do not tie their behavior down so to a specific stimulus. Thus, in this regard, their behavior is, as we have seen, more advanced and neoteric than some other birds. As we have noticed, the more primitive sequences are more tightly tied to specific stimuli.

The mention of parrots and the parrot family always brings up the question of vocalization; this is an interesting problem. Apparenly, vocalization in any of the birds, including the parrot family, is certainly far different from human speech and probably quite different in significant respects from the barks, whines, growls, and cries of mammals. It seems that the vocalization of parrots depends heavily on the chance to mimic the sound in question. Like some other animal cries it also has a strong emotional component. This is evident in the things that parrots learn, whether you want them to or not; swear words, screams, things uttered in emotional tones and often uttered as single exclamations, and the like. We have brought certain vocalizations under control for food reinforcement, but the problem is not quite that simple. The birds in question and with whom we have accomplished this were already talkers. What we did was to bring the specific vocalizations under control with food reinforcement so that they would occur at the proper time. Although we have not experimented very much with vocalization in the parrots, we have not, so far, been successful in shaping the vocalizations with food reinforcement, changing their character, adding words, and so forth. This is not to say that this cannot be done, but we have not so far done it. Mowrer (1960) also experienced considerable difficulty with this problem.

An interesting observation concerning the emotional component of the bird's vocalization: the bit in question consists of a sequence in which the bird picks up a toy telephone, holds it up to his ear, and says "Hello!"—after which he receives a peanut. We noted that every time this particular bird said "Hello," the pupils of his eyes contracted and dilated remarkably. This, of course, is the sort of thing that you would expect in an emotional situation. As soon as the bird was through vocalizing, his pupils returned to normal. People most familiar with these birds note that this sort of thing occurs most often when the vocalizing is connected with showing off. If the bird is merely talking for peanuts, according to Francis Scherr of the Parrot Jungle, in Miami, the pupils may not be affected.

Other interesting observations concerning the psittacines, especially the macaws and cockatoos, which again may reflect their high status in the bird world, is the fluidity of their social organizations. Unlike many of the other birds who have very fixed mating and social patterns, the macaws and cockatoos engage in humanlike behavior. They have homosexual attachments, family fights, divorces, and so on. Here again, in an advanced bird there is a breakdown in "wired in" control. All the bird's behavior is considerably more varied and fluid.

MONKEY BUSINESS

After this look at the primates of the bird world, let us go on briefly to conclude our essay with a few remarks about the true primates. The monkeys and apes have some certain outstanding common characteristics, many of which they share with man. Like the other advanced animals, they are extraordinarily good generalizers. Man has, of course, carried this to an extreme. He can generalize wildly and widely. Although he can discriminate and does, he is first of all a generalizer. He sees bears and chairs in the stars, ships and faces in the clouds, witches and ogres in gnarled trees—resemblances in everything.

Virtually all the primates—monkeys, apes, and men—are noted for their cheap and varied behavior. In some of the monkeys this is almost more obvious than in some of the larger apes. Gorillas, especially the adults, for example, are rather deliberate and lazy in many of their movements. Monkeys are full of monkey business, as are chimpanzees and children. The primates are primarily diurnal animals. They are typically busy all day long, rarely silent, rarely still, except for an occasional resting moment. Certainly this capacity and need for continued activity should be taken into account by anyone who keeps primates in a laboratory situation. Unlike a cat who will philosophically curl up and go to sleep in a cage situation, a monkey desperately needs something to do. The stir-crazy apes who are often seen in zoos are eloquent testimonials to the primate's need for activity, variety, and exercise.

A characteristic apparently common to most if not all of the primates is the faculty of imitation, which is apparently, aside from mimicry observed in bird cries, unique in the animal world. So far as we know, there is nothing like "aping" at the subprimate level except for this mimicry. Many attempts have been made to demonstrate this in other animals, but the phenomenon can usually be traced to other simpler activities. For example, one animal will follow another to an area where food is present. There has never been a well-authenticated, "sure-fire" case of a mammal below the primate level solving a problem through imitation or mimicking another animal except insofar as two animals of the same species with similar backgrounds can be expected to do the same thing at the same time. Although there is insufficient evidence about some of the lower primates, such as the lorises and the other shy little creatures of the tropical forest, and about many of the species of monkeys, most of those observed in captivity apparently have this faculty to some extent. Cathy Hayes (1951) described in her book, *The Ape in Our House,* how she and Dr. Hayes deliberately taught their infant chimpanzee to imitate. They gave the generalized command "Do this," whereupon the chimp was supposed to do anything that the trainer had just done. This resulted in a great deal of control over her behavior. Whether some of the lower primates can manage something like this awaits, of course, experimental tests.

Apparently there are fairly severe limits on control of vocalization in the lower primates, and although the chimpanzee is supposed to have the physical apparatus to make human speech possible, enormously painstaking efforts have never produced anything but a very few words, as witness the Hayes' account of their struggles with Viki. Also many of the vocalizations of the primates, even in an animal as high as the chimpanzee, apparently have a strong instinctive component. The cries are virtually involuntary, as witness Viki's food bark, as reported by the Hayes. The chimp gave herself away when she was trying to steal some cake behind "Mother's" back because her instinctive food bark was so strong that she could not suppress it. Apparently the fluidity and the infinite applicability of the human vocalization is something absolutely unique in the world. As we have noted above (page 84) it is certainly not established that dolphins, for example, have anything remotely resembling human speech in function, variability, or generality.

With regard to sensory capacity, apparently most of the primates have color vision (like many other diurnal animals), although here again evidence is lacking on some of the lower and nocturnal species. Color vision, of course, comes as a great advantage to animals who feed in the daytime and especially animals who live in trees, because it vastly improves their perception of pattern and makes brachiation —swinging from branch to branch—much more accurate. Also the animal is far better equipped to see ground patterns through the leaves. Apparently some evidence is accumulating that the cat may have some color vision. Here again, although primarily nocturnal, the cat is an animal that spends at least part of the time hunting in and from trees. We have preliminary, very tentative experimental evidence that may demonstrate that the squirrel has color vision. It is certainly something to look for wherever you have, first, an animal that spends a good deal of its time in the trees or has in its ancestral evolutionary history been descended from tree-dwelling animals, and, secondly, a primarily diurnal animal.

A good deal of remarkable observational work has been done on social organizations among the primates, indicating that there are quite a variety of types of such organizations (Southwick, 1963). These studies have, of course, obvious applications to human problems and can shed a good deal of light on anthropological studies of our own species.

Some of the most remarkable and significant research in this regard, however, in terms of its implication for human family structure and the nature of human nature, has been coming from Harlow's laboratory at Wisconsin (see reading [5]). In terms of implications for application to the human condition, this series of studies is unique and outstanding in the twentieth century. These studies, which have gone on significantly even beyond the one reprinted in this book, have demonstrated conclusively and succinctly the necessity and nature of mother love, the importance of peer relationships to the growing monkey, the role of father love, and the differences between sexes in the infant monkey. Dr. Harlow remarked in a speech given at the Neuropsychiatric Institute at North Little Rock, Arkansas, that he had discovered boy monkeys were different from girl monkeys; when he reported this to Mrs. Harlow, she commented, "Of course, you should have asked me that in the first place. I could have told you long ago," or as Dr. Harlow noted, male researchers are busy proving things that women have known all along.

Interesting studies have recently been done concerning the abilities of the higher primates to match human achievements. Ferster's studies of "arithmetic" (1964) and similar studies are examples of this sort of thing. However, it is our feeling that the wonderful general capabilities of the primates have not been touched. They are capable of far more than the experimenter has chosen to ask them to do. Especially with understanding of their generalizing tendencies and of the possible pitfalls in setting up discrimination situations in animals with such cheap and varied behavior (as we noted about the dolphins, pages 85–86), we feel that there is room for much more significant research on these animals. With their close behavioral and neurological affinities with man, they can prove as extraordinarily valuable in the experimental study of cultures and higher intellectual processes as they have proven in experimental physiology and medicine.

One explanation of many kinds of primate behavior, particularly human behavior, which we find most useful is the notion that sequences can be reinforcing if they are allowed to go on to completion regardless of their immediate connection with biologically important variables, such as eating, sex, and the like. The opportunity to complete a behavior sequence—to finish a poem, to finish a game, to complete a job—can be as reinforcing to a human being in many cases as the opportunity to eat. Sequences that lead on to other sequences are in themselves reinforcing and can be used in the control of behavior. The cheapness of human and primate behavior in general and the long, long chainings possible mean that enormous amounts of behavior can go on without any direct connection with the primary biological variables. It cannot be said, however, that these sequences do not ultimately have some relation to the primary variables, and indeed in the long evolutionary history of the primates, it can be seen fairly readily how this ability to carry on a long drawn-out sequence of behavior seemingly unrelated to primary drive systems has resulted in the success of these groups. The endless manipulation of objects, the curiosity, the urge to investigate, to "monkey" with things, and the tremendous amount of behavior that man will pour out for very little reason connected with his primitive systems have resulted in his tremendous mastery of the environment, so that when the "chips are down"—when the behavior is needed—he has a large number of previously conditioned sequences, which at the time of learning had little to do with any primary biological variables but which can now be turned to his good use. But in accounting for the behavior itself and the learning of it, we have no need to tie these things elaborately to, or precisely to, the receipt of food, sexual satisfactions, and the like. Although there may be Freudian connotations and sexual significance to music, for example, these are not the whole reason, or necessarily even the primary reason, that some people enjoy playing the piano or listening to a concert.

CHAPTER V

Where Do We Go from Here?

THE PRECEDING CHAPTERS HAVE BEEN INTENDED PRIMA-
rily as a glimpse into the fascinating problems that still await the
serious student of animal behavior in any field, whether he be naturalist or laboratory experimentalist. We hope that some of these more
or less casual observations that need experimental substantiation will
arouse a spark of curiosity in some potential researcher. We feel now
that we can point out some general trends as to the direction that this
research will and should go. In the first place, it should be obvious
by now that there will be a strong cross-disciplinary trend. This
means that the psychology student will need to know not only his
own field but above all biology, zoology, perhaps biochemistry and
anthropology. It should be equally obvious that students in these
other fields will also need to know psychology.

It will also be important, as it is now, for the psychology student
to be rigorously trained in method, in good, clear, hard thinking, in
the pitfalls of anthropomorphism and loose interpretation. However,
it will be important too for him to know the animal and to know that
many wonderful things occur in the animal world that have never
so far been observed in a psychology laboratory.

The second thing that should be obvious is that the study of animal behavior is just in its infancy and is beginning to gain momen-
tum. One previous mention of a few of the species that we have

worked with should indicate the vast number of species that have not been studied at all. Opportunities abound. The fact that there are such striking differences among species means that there is no way for the psychologist to avoid the hard spade work of going out and learning about these various species. Each species may be harboring some nugget of truth, some new insight into behavior as a whole that the psychologist cannot afford to ignore. There is no longer any hope, we believe, that the psychologist can sit in the academic laboratory and study one or two species, generalize a theory of animal behavior from these, and make it apply throughout the animal kingdom. The vast variety of animal behavior and its often situation-specific nature means that species must be studied with all methods available—field observation, comparative methods, and experimental analysis. Particularly we need to relate what the animal is doing in the laboratory to what he does in the wild state.

From the informal and semicontrolled observations reported on various species in the preceding pages, it is apparent that there are many, many species that warrant investigation. For example, there are certain large groups of animals that have been investigated very little either in the laboratory or in the wild: cats, both domestic and wild cats, have been the subjects of very little behavioral study (but see Grossman, 1965). Now that we know a little bit more about the nature of the domestic cat, they can be excellent laboratory subjects; although some experimentalists have used them, particularly in neurological studies, the study of cats needs to be expanded. Field observations of the larger wild cats are certainly indicated, and they can also be studied in semicontrolled conditions in zoos. There are interesting possibilities here for psychologists to study wild animals of all sorts. Garvin McCain, a psychologist at Arlington College, Arlington, Texas, has done some pioneering work in this regard, working in cooperation with the Ft. Worth Zoo, and conducting experiments on some of their large wild animals, none of which have as yet been published. Usually zoos, properly approached, are quite cooperative about studies of this sort. They welcome any information that the psychologist can secure. The effort, however, must be a cooperative one, and the psychologist must honor the zoo's interest in keeping the animals healthy. Thus, any radical experimentation that might affect the well-being of their valuable specimens would not be permissible.

Another group of animals that has been the subject of very little psychological investigation is that of the ungulates. For example, the psychology of the race horse is a fascinating subject. There are very few psychologists who would be able to give a convincing explanation of why a race horse runs at all, and the method of behavioral control used by horse trainers in general is, as we have seen, quite different from that used by operant shapers of behavior. The question of why a horse, and even more remarkably, an elephant, will do the things they do in order to escape the slight flick of a whip, and why they will turn their great bodies in response to the faint pressure of a rein, would represent a fascinating study in avoidance of punishment. Aside from Liddell's work with sheep and goats (Warden, Jenkins, and Warner, II, 1935, pages 347–349), the ungulates as a whole have been largely ignored by psychologists. Although an ordinary psychological laboratory is not very well equipped to house cows, sheep, goats, and deer, again cooperative efforts are possible by working with agricultural departments at the universities and with zoos and wild species of the ungulates (Hafez, 1962).

Another group that is hardy, small, easy to keep, and highly suitable for psychological study is the entire group of the passerine birds. Although certain wild species might prove difficult to keep in captivity because of their emotionality, there are vast numbers that would be quite satisfactory—for example, finches, starlings, sparrows, and canaries.

In addition there are whole realms of work that need to be done on reptiles, amphibians, and insects. It is quite possible that exhaustive psychological studies on some of these simpler animals might yield extraordinary insight into some of the problems of the higher levels.

There is no end of projects to tackle. Many of the semicontrolled observations, reported in these chapters, for example, need to be quantified. A quantitative study needs to be made of the speed and vigor of response in the cat versus the cow at high- and low-drive levels. Grossman (1965) has done such a study, comparing cats and rabbits, with results that have confirmed our observational hunches.

Also quantification might be undertaken on the relative ease of conditioning string pulling in pigeons versus chickens. The problem of vocalization for food has had some experimental investigation but can bear much more. The shaping of vocalization in the psittacines needs to be examined. Also in the case of the chicken, it might be interesting to have a chicken step on a treadle to administer a shock or other noxious stimulus to itself in order to elicit a squawk that would work a sound switch to deliver food. We have noted some of the difficulties about studying punishment in the laboratory: we might study, for example, in the case of the rat what difference we would see if we gave the rat a dark hole to run into as opposed to a lever to press to turn off a shock. With regard to the nature of the reinforcing process, preliminary experiments that we conducted some years ago showed that lead shot poured into a bird's crop cut off the eating behavior even in an extremely hungry bird. In a refinement of this experiment, instead of reinforcing the chicken with food, we might administer, after each response sequence, a slight puff of air into a balloon inserted into the crop, continuing until the balloon is fully inflated. Quantified studies of the hoarding animals are in order. How long will a hamster keep on working if his feed is regularly stolen from him after he disgorges it? Can the presumably more intelligent squirrel be similarly duped?

These are only "teasers." The psychologist who thinks that psychology has reached the end point of its development and that all there is left now is to work out the details with the endless proliferation of experiments under different schedules of reinforcement, schedules of deprivation, and the like, will miss the diversity and richness of animal and human behavior. He may also miss the boat, because the experimental study of animal behavior is in its infancy, and the useful extensibility of the present science to the understanding and control of human behavior is extremely tenuous and dubious.

This is turn brings us to another vista of the future—the role of the animal psychologist in the extension of the science to the human case. In the foregoing pages we have made brief mention of some of the ways in which knowledge of animals can shed light on the condition of *Homo sapiens*. At present our knowledge is so fragmentary that we can largely only guess. But as animal psychologists become widely acquainted with a greater variety of animals and have thoroughly studied their family and social lives, their emotional tendencies—in normal situations and under stress—their instinctive equipment, and the ways in which they can modify their behavior, we may be able to see the human animal in better perspective.

As a few isolated examples, such studies may help reveal to the clinician the role of hereditary emotional make-up in mental illness; possibilities for reinforcement for the extinguished neurotic; new means of eliminating undesirable symptoms. They may help the sociologist discuss intelligently the design of cultures so that they may reduce tensions, capitalize on mankind's built-in tendencies, such as they are, and make the most of woman's talents in a context consistent with her biological and emotional make-up. With the background provided by such studies the anthropologist may better see the significance of the *similarities* rather than the differences between cultures; the ease of conditioning certain behaviors will assume new importance; the ways in which young people assume a culture may have new significance in the handling of our youth. We may better see the significance of critical periods and "imprinting" in childhood for the development of the personality. We may become aware of the necessity of displacement activities to take the place of juvenile delinquency and war—such activities, for example, as football and flights to the moon. These are only hints, but again let us emphasize that one comes to realize what a remarkable animal man is only after long experience with the other animals, and that one cannot understand him fully without this experience and knowledge.

The direction of animal experimentation in the next 25 years may bear scant resemblance to that which laboratory psychology has taken in the last 25 years. We have reached the end of an era in more ways than one and again may find ourselves coming full circle back again to the days of truly comparative psychology. The animal psychologists of the future will be much closer to the biologists, not only in methods but in subject matter and cooperative ties with the biology departments. They will have a much more interesting time of it and will enjoy a wealth of subject matter unknown even to the early comparative psychologists of the turn of the century, because the improvement of communications and travel make available members of vast numbers of species that could be studied only with extreme difficulty earlier in the century.

In understanding the basic business of living in which animals are engaged, the psychologist of the future will be investigating much broader and more significant problems. He will take responsibility for understanding, explaining, and in many cases, control of the entire range of behavior. He will be responsible for accounting for everyday behavior and not be entitled to dismiss certain problems because they do not seem to fit into a certain theoretical system. He can expect, by basing this knowledge on a firm understanding of the basic fundamental problems of animal life, to tie in with the significant problems of human life. The old divisions between human clinical psychology, for example, and the animal experimenters will tend to break down as the animal experimenters have something of true significance to tell the clinician. In short, there is a bold new world awaiting the animal psychologist of the future. It has been there all the time—all we need to do is look at it.

PART TWO

The Selected Readings

IMPORTANT SOURCES INCLUDED IN WHOLE OR IN PART

[1] J. H. Fabre, "The Pine Processionary"
[2] I. P. Pavlov, "Lecture II: Conditioned Reflexes"
[3] F. S. Keller and W. N. Schoenfeld, "Operant Conditioning"
[4] K. Z. Lorenz, "The Taming of the Shrew"
[5] H. F. Harlow, "The Nature of Love"

[1]

The Pine Processionary

J. HENRI FABRE

In my *harmas* laboratory, now stocked with a few trees in addition to its bushes, stand some vigorous fir-trees, the Aleppo pine and the black Austrian pine, a substitute for that of the Landes. Every year the caterpillar takes possession of them and spins his great purses in their branches. In the interest of the leaves, which are horribly ravaged, as though there had been a fire, I am obliged each winter to make a strict survey and to extirpate the nests with a long forked batten.

You voracious little creatures, if I let you have your way, I should soon be robbed of the murmur of my once so leafy pines! Today I will seek compensation for all the trouble I have taken. Let us make a compact. You have a story to tell. Tell it me; and for a year, for two years or longer, until I know more or less all about it, I shall leave you undisturbed, even at the cost of lamentable suffering to the pines.

Having concluded the treaty and left the caterpillars in peace, I soon have abundant material for my observations. In return for my indulgence I get some thirty nests within a few steps of my door. If the collection were not large enough, the pine trees in the neighbourhood would supply me with any necessary additions. But I have a preference and a decided preference for the population of my own enclosure, whose nocturnal habits are much easier to observe by lantern-light. With such treasures daily before my eyes, at any time that I wish and under natural conditions, I cannot fail to see the Processionary's story unfolded at full length. Let us try.

Drover Dingdong's Sheep followed the Ram which Panurge had maliciously thrown overboard and leapt nimbly into the sea, one

SOURCE: Reprinted by permission of Dodd, Mead & Company from *The Insect World of J. Henri Fabre* by Edwin Way Teale (ed.). Copyright, 1916, by Dodd, Mead & Company, Inc. Copyright, 1949, by Edwin Way Teale.

after the other, "for you know," says Rabelais, "it is the nature of the sheep always to follow the first, wheresoever it goes; which makes Aristotle mark them for the most silly and foolish animals in the world."

The Pine Caterpillar is even more sheeplike, not from foolishness, but from necessity: where the first goes all the others go, in a regular string, with no empty spaces.

They proceed in single file, in a continuous row, each touching with its head the rear of the one in front of it. The complex twists and turns described in his vagaries by the caterpillar leading the van are scrupulously described by all the others. No Greek theoria winding its way to the Eleusinian festivals was ever more orderly. Hence the name of Processionary given to the gnawer of the pine.

His character is complete when we add that he is a ropedancer all his life long: he walks only on the tight-rope, a silken rail placed in position as he advances. The caterpillar who chances to be at the head of the procession dribbles his thread without ceasing and fixes it on the path which his fickle preferences cause him to take. The thread is so tiny that the eyes, though armed with a magnifying glass, suspects it rather than sees it.

But a second caterpillar steps on the slender footboard and doubles it with his thread; a third trebles it; and all the others, however many there be, add the sticky spray from their spinnerets, so much so that, when the procession has marched by, there remains, as a record of its passing, a narrow white ribbon whose dazzling whiteness shimmers in the sun. Very much more sumptuous than ours, their system of road-making consists in upholstering with silk instead of macadamizing. We sprinkle our roads with broken stones and level them by the pressure of a heavy steamroller; they lay over their paths a soft satin rail, a work of general interest to which each contributes his thread.

What is the use of all this luxury? Could they not, like other caterpillars, walk about without these costly preparations? I see two reasons for their mode of progression. It is night when the Processionaries sally forth to browse upon the pine-leaves. They leave their nest, situated at the top of a bough, in profound darkness; they go down the denuded pole till they come to the nearest branch that has not yet been gnawed, a branch which becomes lower and lower by degrees as the consumers finish stripping the upper storeys; they climb up this untouched branch and spread over the green needles.

When they have had their suppers and begin to feel the keen night air, the next thing is to return to the shelter of the house. Measured in a straight line, the distance is not great, hardly an arm's length; but it cannot be covered in this way on foot. The caterpillars have to climb down from one crossing to the next, from the needle to the twig, from the twig to the branch, from the branch to the bough and from the bough, by a no less angular path, to go back home. It is useless to rely upon sight as a guide on this long and erratic journey. The Processionary, it is true, has five ocular specks on either side of his head, but they are so infinitesimal, so difficult to make out through the magnifying glass, that we cannot attribute to them any great power of vision. Besides, what good would those short-sighted lenses be in the absence of light, in black darkness?

It is equally useless to think of the sense of smell. Has the Processional any olfactory powers or has he not? I do not know. Without giving a positive answer to the question, I can at least declare that his sense of smell is exceedingly dull and in no way suited to help him find his way. This is proved, in my experiments, by a number of hungry caterpillars that, after a long fast, pass close beside a pine-branch without betraying any eagerness or showing a sign of stopping. It is the sense of touch that tells them where they are. So long as their lips do not chance to light upon the pasture-land, not one of them settles there, though he be ravenous. They do not hasten to food which they have scented from afar; they stop at a branch which they encounter on their way.

Apart from sight and smell, what remains to guide them in returning to the nest? The ribbon spun on the road. In the Cretan labyrinth, Theseus would have been lost but for the clue of thread with which Ariadne supplied him. The spreading maze of the pine-needles is, especially at night, as inextricable a labyrinth as that constructed for Minos. The Processionary finds his way through it, without the possibility of a mistake, by the aid of his bit of silk. At the time for going home, each easily recovers either his own thread or one or other of the neighbouring threads, spread fanwise by the diverging herd; one by one the scattered tribe line up on the common ribbon, which started from the nest; and the sated caravan finds its way back to the manor with absolute certainty.

Longer expeditions are made in the daytime, even in winter, if the weather be fine. Our caterpillars then come down from the tree, venture on the ground, march in procession for a distance of thirty yards or so. The object of these sallies is not to look for food, for the native pine-tree is far from being exhausted: the shorn branches hardly count amid the vast leafage. Moreover, the caterpillars observe complete abstinence till nightfall. The trippers have no other object than a constitutional, a pilgrimage to the outskirts to see what these are like, possibly an inspection of the locality where, later, they mean to bury themselves in the sand for their metamorphosis.

It goes without saying that, in these greater evolutions, the guiding cord is not neglected. It is now more necessary than ever. All contribute to it from the produce of their spinnerets, as is the invariable rule whenever there is a progression. Not one takes a step forward without fixing to the path the thread hanging from his lip.

If the series forming the procession be at all long, the ribbon is dilated sufficiently to make it easy to find; nevertheless, on the homeward journey, it is not picked up without some hesitation. For observe that the caterpillars when on the march never turn completely; to wheel round on their tight-rope is a method utterly unknown to them. In order therefore to regain the road already covered, they have to describe a zig-zag whose windings and extent are determined by the leader's fancy. Hence come gropings and roamings which are sometimes prolonged to the point of causing the herd to spend the night out of doors. It is not a serious matter. They collect into a motionless cluster. Tomorrow the search will start afresh and will sooner or later be successful. Oftener still the winding curve meets the guide-thread at the first attempt. As soon as the first caterpillar has the rail between his legs, all hesitation ceases; and the band makes for the nest with hurried steps.

The use of this silk-tapestried roadway is evident from a second point of view. To protect himself against the severity of the winter which he has to face when working, the Pine Caterpillar weaves himself a shelter in which he spends his bad hours, his days of enforced idleness. Alone, with none but the meagre resources of his silk-glands, he would find difficulty in protecting himself on the top of a branch buffeted by the winds. A substantial dwelling, proof against snow, gales and icy fogs, requires the cooperation of a large number. Out of the individual's piled-up atoms, the community obtains a spacious and durable establishment.

The enterprise takes a long time to complete. Every evening, when the weather permits, the building has to be strengthened and enlarged. It is indispensable, therefore, that the corporation of workers should not be dissolved while the stormy season continues and the insects are still in the caterpillar stage. But, without special arrangements, each nocturnal expedition at grazing-time would be a cause of separation. At that moment of appetite for food there is a return to individualism. The caterpillars become more or less scattered, settling singly on the branches around; each browses his pine-needle separately. How are they to find one another afterwards and become a community again?

The several threads left on the road make this easy. With that guide, every caterpillar, however far he may be, comes back to his companions without ever missing the way. They come hurrying from a host of twigs, from here, from there, from above, from below; and soon the scattered legion reforms into a group. The silk thread is something more than a road-making expedient; it is the social bond, the system that keeps the members of the community indissolubly united.

At the head of every procession, long or short, goes a first caterpillar whom I will call the leader of the march or file, though the word leader, which I use for want of a better, is a little out of place here. Nothing, in fact, distinguishes this caterpillar from the others: it just depends upon the order in which they happen to line up; and mere chance brings him to the front. Among the Processionaries, every captain is an officer of fortune. The actual leader leads; presently he will be a subaltern, if the file should break up in consequence of some accident and be formed anew in a different order.

His temporary functions give him an attitude of his own. While the others follow passively in a close file, he, the captain, tosses himself about and with an abrupt movement flings the front of his body hither and thither. As he marches ahead he seems to be seeking his way. Does he in point of fact explore the country? Does he choose the most practicable places? Or are his hesitations merely the result of the absence of a guiding thread on ground that has not yet been covered? His subordinates follow very placidly, reassured by the cord which they hold between their legs; he, deprived of that support, is uneasy.

Why cannot I read what passes under his black, shiny skull, so like a drop of tar? To judge by actions, there is here a small dose of discernment which is able, after experimenting, to recognize excessive roughnesses, over-slippery surfaces, dusty places that offer no resistance and, above all, the thread left by other excursionists. This is all or nearly all that my long acquaintance with the Processionaries has taught me as to their mentality. Poor brains, indeed; poor creatures, whose commonwealth has its safety hanging upon a thread!

The processions vary greatly in length. The finest that I have seen manoeuvring on the ground measured twelve or thirteen yards and numbered about three hundred caterpillars, drawn up with absolute precision in a wavy line. But, if there were only two in a row, the order would still be perfect: the second touches and follows the first.

By February I have processions of all lengths in the greenhouse. What tricks can I play upon them? I see only two: to do away with the leader; and to cut the thread.

The suppression of the leader of the file produces nothing striking. If the thing is done without creating a disturbance, the procession does not alter its way at all. The second caterpillar, promoted to captain, knows the duties of his rank offhand: he selects and leads, or rather he hesitates and gropes.

The breaking of the silk ribbon is not very important either. I remove a caterpillar from the middle of the file. With my scissors, so as not to cause a commotion in the ranks, I cut the piece of ribbon on which he stood and clear away every thread of it. As a result of this breach, the procession acquires two marching leaders, each independent of the other. It may be that the one in the rear joins the file ahead of him, from which he is separated by but a slender interval; in that case, things return to their original condition. More frequently, the two parts do not become reunited. In that case, we have two distinct processions, each of which wanders where it pleases and diverges from the other. Nevertheless, both will be able to return to the nest by discovering sooner or later, in the course of their peregrinations, the ribbon on the other side of the break.

These two experiments are only moderately interesting. I have thought out another, one more fertile in possibilities. I propose to make the caterpillars describe a closed circuit, after the ribbons running from it and liable to bring about a change of direction have been destroyed. The locomotive engine pursues its invariable course so long as it is not shunted on to a branch-line. If the Processionaries find the silken rail always clear in front of them, with no switches anywhere, will they continue on the same track, will they persist in following a road that never comes to an end? What we have to do is to produce this circuit, which is unknown under ordinary conditions, by artificial means.

The first idea that suggests itself is to seize with the forceps the silk ribbon at the back of the train, to bend it without shaking it and to bring the end of it ahead of the file. If the caterpillar marching in the van steps upon it, the thing is done: the others will follow him faithfully. The operation is very simple in theory but very difficult in practice and produces no useful results. The ribbon, which is extremely slight, breaks under the weight of the grains of sand that stick to it and are lifted with it. If it does not break, the caterpillars at the back, however delicately we may go to work, feel a disturbance which makes them curl up or even let go.

There is a yet greater difficulty: the leader refuses the ribbon laid before him; the cut end makes him distrustful. Failing to see the regular, uninterrupted road, he slants off to the right or left, he escapes at a tangent. If I try to interfere and to bring him back to the path of my choosing, he persists in his refusal, shrivels up, does not budge; and soon the whole procession is in confusion. We will not insist: the method is a poor one, very wasteful of effort for at best a problematical success.

We ought to interfere as little as possible and obtain a natural closed circuit. Can it be done? Yes. It lies in our power, without the least meddling, to see a procession march along a perfect circular track. I owe this result, which is eminently deserving of our attention, to pure chance.

On the shelf with the layer of sand in which the nests are planted stand some big palm-vases measuring nearly a yard and a half in circumference at the top. The caterpillars often scale the sides and climb up to the moulding which forms a cornice around the opening. This place suits them for their processions, perhaps because of the absolute firmness of the surface, where there is no fear of landslides, as on the loose, sandy soil below; and also, perhaps because of the horizontal position, which is favorable to repose after the fatigue of the ascent. It provides me with a circular track all ready-made. I have nothing to do but wait for an occasion propitious to my plans. This occasion is not long in coming.

On the 30th of January, 1896, a little before twelve o'clock in the day, I discover a numerous troop making their way up and gradually reaching the popular cornice. Slowly, in a single file, the caterpillars climb the great vase, mount the ledge and advance in regular procession, while others are constantly arriving and continuing the series. I wait for the string to close up, that is to say, for the leader, who keeps following the circular moulding, to return to the point from which he started. My object is achieved in a quarter of an hour. The closed circuit is realized magnificently, in something very nearly approaching a circle.

The next thing is to get rid of the rest of the ascending column, which would disturb the fine order of the procession by an excess of newcomers; it is also important that we should do away with all the silken paths, both new and old, that can put the cornice into communication with the ground. With a thick hair-pencil I sweep away the surplus climbers; with a big brush, one that leaves no smell behind it—for this might afterwards prove confusing—I carefully rub down the vase and get rid of every thread which the caterpillars have laid on the march. When these preparations are finished, a curious sight awaits us.

In the uninterrupted circular procession there is no longer a leader. Each caterpillar is preceded by another on whose heels he follows, guided by the silk track, the work of the whole party; he again has a companion close behind him, following him in the same orderly way. And this is repeated without variation throughout the length of the chain. None commands, or rather none modifies the trail according to his fancy; all obey, trusting in the guide who ought normally to lead the march and who in reality has been abolished by my trickery.

From the first circuit of the edge of the tub the rail of silk has been laid in position and is soon turned into a narrow ribbon by the procession, which never ceases dribbling its thread as it goes. The rail is simply doubled and has no branches anywhere, for my brush has destroyed them all. What will the caterpillars do on this deceptive, closed path? Will they walk endlessly round and round until their strength gives out entirely?

The old schoolmen were fond of quoting Buridan's Ass, that famous Donkey who, when placed between two bundles of hay, starved to death because he was unable to decide in favour of either by breaking the equilibrium between two equal but opposite attractions. They slandered the worthy animal. The Ass, who is no more foolish than any one else, would reply to the logical snare by feasting off both bundles. Will my caterpillars show a little of his mother wit? Will they, after many attempts, be able to break the equilibrium of their closed circuit. which keeps them on a road without a turning? Will they make up their minds to swerve to this side or that, which is the only method of reaching their bundle of hay, the green branch yonder, quite near, not two feet off?

I thought that they would and I was wrong. I said to myself:

"The procession will go on turning for some time, for an hour, two hours perhaps; then the caterpillars will perceive their mistake. They will abandon the deceptive road and make their descent somewhere or other."

That they should remain up there, hard pressed by hunger and the lack of cover, when nothing prevented them from going away, seemed to me inconceivable imbecility. Facts, however, forced me to accept the incredible. Let us describe them in detail.

The circular procession begins, as I have said, on the 30th of January, about midday, in splendid weather. The caterpillars march at an even pace, each touching the stern of the one in front of him. The unbroken chain eliminates the leader with his changes of direction; and all follow mechanically, as faithful to their circle as are the hands of a watch. The headless file has no liberty left, no will; it has become mere clockwork. And this continues for hours and hours. My success goes far beyond my wildest suspicions. I stand amazed at it, or rather I am stupefied.

Meanwhile, the multiplied circuits change the original rail into a superb ribbon a twelfth of an inch broad. I can easily see it glittering on the red ground of the pot. The day is drawing to a close and no alteration has yet taken place in the position of the trail. A striking proof confirms this.

The trajectory is not a plane curve, but one which, at a certain point, deviates and goes down a little way to the lower surface of the cornice, returning to the top some eight inches farther. I marked these two points of deviation in pencil on the vase at the outset. Well, all that afternoon and, more conclusive still, on the following days, right to the end of this mad dance, I see the string of caterpillars dip under the ledge at the first point and come to the top again at the second. Once the first thread is laid, the road to be pursued is permanently established.

If the road does not vary, the speed does. I measure nine centimetres a minute as the average distance covered. But there are more or less lengthy halts; the pace slackens at times, especially when the temperature falls. At ten o'clock in the evening the walk is a little more than a lazy swaying of the body. I foresee an early halt, in consequence of the cold, of fatigue and doubtless also of hunger.

Grazing-time has arrived. The caterpillars have come crowding from all the nests in the greenhouse to browse upon the pine-branches planted by myself beside the silken purses. Those in the garden do the same, for the temperature is mild. The others, lined up along the earthenware cornice, would gladly take part in the feast; they are bound to have an appetite after a ten hours' walk. The branch stands green and tempting not a hand's breadth away. To reach it they need but go down; and the poor wretches, foolish slaves of their ribbon that they are, cannot make up their minds to do so. I leave the famished ones at half-past ten, persuaded that they will take counsel with the pillow and that on the morrow things will have resumed their ordinary course.

I was wrong. I was expecting too much of them when I accorded them that faint gleam of intelligence which the tribulations of a distressful stomach ought, one would think, to have aroused. I visit them at dawn. They are lined up as on the day before, but motionless. When the air grows a little warmer, they shake off their torpor, revive and start walking again. The circular procession begins anew, like that which I have already seen. There is nothing more and nothing less to be noted in their machine-like obstinacy.

This time it is a bitter night. A cold snap has supervened, was indeed foretold in the evening by the garden caterpillars, who refused to come out despite appearances which to my duller senses seemed to promise a continuation of the fine weather. At daybreak the rosemary-walks are all asparkle with rime and for the second time this year there is a sharp frost. The large pond in the garden is frozen over. What can the caterpillars in the conservatory be doing?

All are ensconced in their nests, except the stubborn processionists on the edge of the vase, who, deprived of shelter as they are, seem to have spent a very bad night. I find them clustered in two heaps, without any attempt at order. They have suffered less from the cold, thus huddled together.

'Tis an ill wind that blows nobody any good. The severity of the night has caused the ring to break into two segments which will, perhaps, afford a chance of safety. Each group, as it revives and resumes its walk, will presently be headed by a leader who, not being obliged to follow a caterpillar in front of him, will possess some liberty of movement and perhaps be able to make the procession swerve to one side. Remember that, in the ordinary processions, the caterpillar walking ahead acts as a scout. While the others, if nothing occurs to create excitement, keep to their ranks, he attends to his duties as a leader and is continually turning his head to this side and that, investigating, seeking, groping, making his choice. And things happen as he decides: the band follows him faithfully. Remember also that, even on a road which has already been travelled and beribboned, the guiding caterpillar continues to explore.

There is reason to believe that the Processionaries who have lost their way on the ledge will find a chance of safety here. Let us watch them. On recovering from their torpor, the two groups line up by degrees into two distinct files. There are therefore two leaders, free to go where they please, independent of each other. Will they succeed in leaving the enchanted circle? At the sight of their large black heads swaying anxiously from side to side, I am inclined to think so for a moment. But I am soon undeceived. As the ranks fill out, the two sections of the chain meet and the circle is reconstituted. The momentary leaders once more become simple subordinates; and again the caterpillars march round and round all day.

For the second time in succession, the night, which is very calm and magnificently starry, brings a hard frost. In the morning the Processionaries on the tub, the only ones who have camped out unsheltered, are gathered into a heap which largely overflows both sides of the fatal ribbon. I am present at the awakening of the numbed ones. The first to take the road is, as luck will have it, outside the track. Hesitatingly he ventures into unknown ground. He reaches the top of the rim and descends upon the other side on the earth in the vase. He is followed by six others, no more. Perhaps the rest of the troop, who have not fully recovered from their nocturnal torpor, are too lazy to bestir themselves.

The result of this brief delay is a return to the old track. The caterpillars embark on the silken trail and the circular march is resumed, this time in the form of a ring with a gap in it. There is no attempt, however, to strike a new course on the part of the guide whom this gap has placed at the head. A chance of stepping outside the magic circle has presented itself at last; and he does not know how to avail himself of it.

As for the caterpillars who have made their way to the inside of the vase, their lot is hardly improved. They climb to the top of the palm, starving and seeking for food. Finding nothing to eat that suits them, they retrace their steps by following the thread which they have left on the way, climb the ledge of the pot, strike the procession again and, without further anxiety, slip back into the ranks. Once more the ring is complete, once more the circle turns and turns.

Then when will the deliverance come? There is a legend that tells of poor souls dragged along in an endless round until the hellish charm is broken by a drop of holy water. What drop will good fortune sprinkle on my Processionaries to dissolve their circle and bring them back to the nest? I see only two means of conjuring the spell and obtaining a release from the circuit. These two means are two painful ordeals. A strange linking of cause and effect: from sorrow and wretchedness good is to come.

And, first, shrivelling as the result of cold, the caterpillars gather together without any order, heap themselves some on the path, some, more numerous these, outside it. Among the latter there may be, sooner or later, some revolutionary who, scorning the beaten track, will trace out a new road and lead the troop back home. We have just seen an instance of it. Seven penetrated to the interior of the vase and climbed the palm. True, it was an attempt with no result, but still an attempt. For complete success, all that need be done would have been to take the opposite slope. An even chance is a great thing. Another time we shall be more successful.

In the second place, the exhaustion due to fatigue and hunger. A lame one stops, unable to go farther. In front of the defaulter the procession still continues to wend its way for a short time. The ranks close up and an empty space appears. On coming to himself and resuming the march, the caterpillar who has caused the breach becomes a leader, having nothing before him. The least desire for emancipation is all that he wants to make him launch the band into a new path which perhaps will be the saving path.

In short, when the Processionaries' train is in difficulties, what it needs, unlike ours, is to run off the rails. The side-tracking is left to the caprice of a leader who alone is capable of turning to the right or left; and this leader is absolutely nonexistent so long as the ring remains unbroken. Lastly, the breaking of the circle, the one stroke of luck, is the result of a chaotic halt, caused principally by excess of fatigue or cold.

The liberating accident, especially that of fatigue, occurs fairly often. In the course of the same day, the moving circumference is cut up several times into two or three sections; but continuity soon returns and no change takes place. Things go on just the same. The bold innovator who is to save the situation has not yet had his inspiration.

There is nothing new on the fourth day, after an icy night like the previous one; nothing to tell except the following detail. Yesterday I did not remove the trace left by the few caterpillars who made their way to the inside of the vase. This trace, together with a junction connecting it with the circular road, is discovered in the course of the morning. Half the troop takes advantage of it to visit the earth in the pot and climb the palm; the other half remains on the ledge and continues to walk along the old rail. In the afternoon the band of emigrants rejoins the others, the circuit is completed and things return to their original condition.

We come to the fifth day. The night frost becomes more intense, without however as yet reaching the greenhouse. It is followed by bright sunshine in a calm and limpid sky. As soon as the sun's rays have warmed the panes a little, the caterpillars, lying in heaps, wake up and resume their evolutions on the ledge of the vase. This time the fine order of the beginning is disturbed and a certain disorder becomes manifest, apparently an omen of deliverance near at hand. The scouting-path inside the vase, which was upholstered in silk yesterday and the day before, is to-day followed to its origin on the rim by a part of the band and is then abandoned after a short loop. The other caterpillars follow the usual ribbon. The result of this bifurcation is two almost equal files, walking along the ledge in the same direction, at a short distance from each other, sometimes meeting, separating farther on, in every case with some lack of order.

Weariness increases the confusion. The crippled, who refuse to go on, are many. Breaches increase; files are split up into sections each of which has its leader, who pokes the front of his body this way and that to explore the ground. Everything seems to point to the disintegration which will bring safety. My hopes are once more disappointed. Before the night the file is reconstituted and the gyration resumed.

Heat comes, just as suddenly as the cold did. Today, the 4th of February, is a beautiful, mild day. The greenhouse is full of life. Numerous festoons of caterpillars, issuing from the nests, meander along the sand on the shelf. Above them, at every moment, the ring on the ledge of the vase breaks up and comes together again. For the first time I see daring leaders who, drunk with heat, standing only on their hinder prolegs at the extreme edge of the earthenware rim, fling themselves forward into space, twisting about, sounding the depths. The endeavour is frequently repeated, while the whole troop stops. The caterpillars' heads give sudden jerks; their bodies wriggle.

One of the pioneers decides to take the plunge. He slips under the ledge. Four follow him. The others, still confiding in the perfidious silken path, dare not copy him and continue to go along the old road.

The short string detached from the general chain gropes about a great deal, hesitates long on the side of the vase; it goes half-way down, then climbs up again slantwise, rejoins and takes its place in the procession. This time the attempt has failed, though at the foot of the vase, not nine inches away, there lay a bunch of pine-needles which I had placed there with the object of enticing the hungry ones. Smell and sight told them nothing. Near as they were to the goal, they went up again.

No matter, the endeavour has its uses. Threads were laid on the way and will serve as a lure to further enterprise. The road of deliverance has its first landmarks. And two days later, on the eighth day of the experiment, the caterpillars—now singly, anon in small groups, then again in strings of some length—come down from the ledge by following the staked-out path. At sunset the last of the laggards is back in the nest.

Now for a little arithmetic. For seven times twenty-four hours the caterpillars have remained on the ledge of the vase. To make an ample allowance for stops due to the weariness of this one or that and above all for the rest taken during the colder hours of the night, we will deduct one-half of the time. This leaves eighty-four hours' walking. The average pace is nine centimetres a minute. The aggregate distance covered, therefore, is 433 metres, a good deal more than a quarter of a mile, which is a great walk for these little crawlers. The circumference of the vase, the perimeter of the track, is exactly 1 m. 35. Therefore the circle covered, always in the same direction and always without result, was described three hundred and thirty-five times.

These figures surprise me, though I am already familiar with the abysmal stupidity of insects as a class whenever the least accident occurs. I feel inclined to ask myself whether the Processionaries were not kept up there so long by the difficulties and dangers of the descent rather than by the lack of any gleam of intelligence in their benighted minds. The facts, however, reply that the descent is as easy as the ascent.

The caterpillar has a very supple back, well adapted for twisting round projections or slipping underneath. He can walk with the same ease vertically or horizontally, with his back down or up. Besides, he never moves forward until he has fixed his thread to the ground. With this support to his feet, he has no falls to fear, no matter what his position.

I had a proof of this before my eyes during a whole week. As I have already said, the track, instead of keeping on one level, bends twice, dips at a certain point under the ledge of the vase and reappears at the top a little farther on. At one part of the circuit, therefore, the procession walks on the lower surface of the rim; and this inverted position implies so little discomfort or danger that it is renewed at each turn for all the caterpillars from first to last.

It is out of the question then to suggest the dread of a false step on the edge of the rim which is so nimbly turned at each point of inflexion. The caterpillars in distress, starved, shelterless, chilled with cold at night, cling obstinately to the silk ribbon covered hundreds of times, because they lack the rudimentary glimmers of reason which would advise them to abandon it.

[2]

Lecture II: Conditioned Reflexes

I. P. PAVLOV

*Technical methods employed in the objective investigation of the func-
tions of the cerebral hemispheres.—Response to signals as reflex action.—
Unconditioned and conditioned reflexes.—Necessary conditions for the
development of conditioned reflexes.*

In the previous lecture I gave an account of the reasons which
led us to adopt, for the investigation of the functions of the cerebral
hemispheres, the purely objective method used for investigating
the physiological activity of the lower parts of the nervous system.
In this manner the investigation of the cerebral hemispheres is
brought into line with the investigations conducted in other branches
of natural science, and their activities are studied as purely physiological facts, without any need to resort to fantastic speculations as
to the existence of any possible subjective state in the animal which
may be conjectured on analogy with ourselves. From this point of
view the whole nervous activity of the animal must be regarded as
based firstly on inborn reflexes. These are regular causal connections
between certain definite external stimuli acting on the organism
and its necessary reflex reactions. Such inborn reflexes are comparatively few in number, and the stimuli setting them in action act
close up, being as a rule the general physical and chemical properties of the common agencies which affect the organism. The inborn
reflexes by themselves are inadequate to ensure the continued
existence of the organism, especially of the more highly organized
animals, which, when deprived of their highest nervous activity,
are permanently disabled, and if left to themselves, although retain-
ing all their inborn reflexes, soon cease to exist. The complex conditions of everyday existence require a much more detailed and

SOURCE: I. P. Pavlov, Lecture II, "Technical Methods," from *Conditioned
Reflexes* (New York: Dover Publications, 1960.) Reprinted by permission of
The Clarendon Press, Oxford.

specialized correlation between the animal and its environment than is afforded by the inborn reflexes alone. This more precise correlation can be established only through the medium of the cerebral hemispheres; and we have found that a great number of all sorts of stimuli always act through the medium of the hemispheres as temporary and interchangeable signals for the comparatively small number of agencies of a general character which determine the inborn reflexes, and that this is the only means by which a most delicate adjustment of the organism to the environment can be established. To this function of the hemispheres we gave the name of "signalization."

Before passing on to describe the results of our investigation it is necessary to give some account of the purely technical side of the methods employed, and to describe the general way in which the signalizing activity of the hemispheres can be studied. It is obvious that the reflex activity of any effector organ can be chosen for the purpose of this investigation, since signalling stimuli can get linked up with any of the inborn reflexes. But, as was mentioned in the first lecture, the starting point for the present investigation was determined in particular by the study of two reflexes—the food or "alimentary" reflex, and the "defence" reflex in its mildest form, as observed when a rejectable substance finds its way into the mouth of the animal. As it turned out, these two reflexes proved a fortunate choice in many ways. Indeed, while any strong defence reflex, for example, against such a stimulus as a powerful electric current, makes the animal extremely restless and excited; and while the sexual reflexes require a special environment—to say nothing of their periodic character and their dependence upon age—the alimentary reflex and the mild defence reflex to rejectable substances are normal everyday occurrences.

It is essential to realize that each of these two reflexes—the alimentary reflex and the mild defence reflex to rejectable substances —consists of two distinct components, a motor and a secretory. Firstly the animal exhibits a reflex activity directed towards getting hold of the food and eating it or, in the case of rejectable substances, towards getting rid of them out of the mouth; and secondly, in both cases an immediate secretion of saliva occurs, in the case of food, to start the physical and chemical processes of digestion and, in the case of rejectable substances, to wash them out of the mouth. We confined our experiments almost entirely to the secretory component of the reflex: the allied motor reactions were taken into account only where there were special reasons. The secretory reflex presents many important advantages for our purpose. It allows of an extremely accurate measurement of the intensity of reflex activity, since either the number of drops in a given time may be counted or else the saliva may be caused to displace a coloured fluid in a horizontally placed graduated glass tube. It would be much more difficult to obtain the same accuracy of measurement for any motor reflex, especially for such complex motor reactions as accompany reflexes to food or to rejectable substances. Even by using most delicate instruments we should never be able to reach such precision in measuring the intensity of the motor component of the reflexes as can easily be attained with the secretory component. Again, a very important point in favour of the secretory reflexes is the much smaller tendency to interpret them in an anthropomorphic fashion—that is, in terms of subjective analogy. Although this seems a trivial consideration from our present standpoint, it was of importance in the earlier stages of our investigation and did undoubtedly influence our choice.

For the purpose of registering the intensity of the salivary reflex all the dogs employed in the experiments are subjected to a preliminary minor operation, which consists in the transplantation of the opening of the salivary duct from its natural place on the mucous membrane of the mouth to the outside skin. For this purpose the terminal portion of the salivary duct is dissected and freed from the surrounding tissue, and the duct, together with a small portion of the mucous membrane surrounding its natural opening, is carried through a suitable incision, to the outside of the cheek in the case of the parotid gland, or under the chin in the case of the submaxillary gland. In this new position the duct is fixed by a few stitches which are removed when the wound has healed. As a result of the operation the saliva now flows to the outside, on to the cheek or chin of the animal, instead of into the mouth, so that the measurement of the secretory activity of the gland is greatly facilitated. It is only necessary for this purpose to adjust a small glass funnel over the opening of the duct on to the skin, and for this we find a special cement prepared according to a formula of Mendeléeff [1] most useful. As an alternative, very suitable and accurate as a recording apparatus is a hemispherical bulb which also can be hermetically sealed on to the skin. From the bulb project two tubes, one pointing up and the other pointing down. The latter tube is used for drawing off the saliva which collects during each observation, while the former tube connects by air transmission with a horizontal graduated glass tube filled with coloured fluid. As the saliva flows into the hemispherical bulb the coloured fluid is displaced along the graduated tube, where the amount of secretion can be read off accurately. Further, it is not difficult to fix up an automatic electrically-recording device which will split up the displaced fluid into drops of exactly equal volume and reduce any lag in the movement of the fluid to a minimum.[2]

To come to the general technique of the experiments, it is important to remember that our research deals with the highly specialized activity of the cerebral cortex, a signalizing apparatus of tremendous complexity and of most exquisite sensitivity, through which the animal is influenced by countless stimuli from the outside world. Every one of these stimuli produces a certain effect upon the animal, and all of them taken together may clash and interfere with, or else reinforce, one another. Unless we are careful to take special precautions the success of the whole investigation may be jeopardized, and we should get hopelessly lost as soon as we begin to seek for cause and effect among so many and various influences, so intertwined and entangled as to form a veritable chaos. It was evident that the experimental conditions had to be

---

[1] *Mendeléeff's cement:* Colophonium, 50 grammes; ferric oxide, 40 grammes; yellow beeswax, 25 grammes.

[2] In almost all the experiments quoted in these lectures the amount of salivary secretion is, for the sake of uniformity, given in drops. It was, however, only in the very earliest period of the research—before the separation of the experimenter from the animal was made—that the actual number of drops falling from a small funnel fixed over the fistula was counted, and only a few of these experiments are given. In the great majority of the experiments the salivary secretion was measured by the displacement of water in a graduated tube or by the electric recorder, allowing a much greater accuracy of measurement. The readings so obtained have been converted, in the tables, into drops. Thus, in some experiments it will be noticed that the number of drops is given to an accuracy of one-tenth.

simplified, and that this simplification must consist in eliminating as far as possible any stimuli outside our control which might fall upon the animal, admitting only such stimuli as could be entirely controlled by the experimenter. It was thought at the beginning of our research that it would be sufficient simply to isolate the experimenter in the research chamber with the dog on its stand, and to refuse admission to anyone else during the course of an experiment. But this precaution was found to be wholly inadequate, since the experimenter, however still he might try to be, was himself a constant source of a large number of stimuli. His slightest movements —blinking of the eyelids or movement of the eyes, posture, respiration and so on—all acted as stimuli which, falling upon the dog, were sufficient to vitiate the experiments by making exact interpretation of the results extremely difficult. In order to exclude this undue influence on the part of the experimenter as far as possible, he had to be stationed outside the room in which the dog was placed, and even this precaution proved unsuccessful in laboratories not specially designed for the study of these particular reflexes. The environment of the animal, even when shut up by itself in a room, is perpetually changing. Footfalls of a passer-by, chance conversations in neighbouring rooms, slamming of a door or vibration from a passing van, street-cries, even shadows cast through the windows into the room, any of these casual uncontrolled stimuli falling upon the receptors of the dog set up a disturbance in the cerebral hemispheres and vitiate the experiments. To get over all these disturbing factors a special laboratory was built at the Institute of Experimental Medicine in Petrograd, the funds being provided by a keen and public-spirited Moscow business man. The primary task was the protection of the dogs from uncontrolled extraneous stimuli, and this was effected by surrounding the building with an isolating trench and employing other special structural devices. Inside the building all the research rooms (four to each floor) were isolated from one another by a cross-shaped corridor; the top and ground floors, where these rooms were situated, were separated by an intermediate floor. Each research room was carefully partitioned by the use of sound-proof materials into two compartments—one for the animal, the other for the experimenter. For stimulating the animal, and for registering the corresponding reflex response, electrical methods or pneumatic transmission were used. By means of these arrangements it was possible to get something of that stability of environmental conditions so essential to the carrying out of a successful experiment.

Another point should be mentioned—although in this respect the means at our disposal still leave something to be desired. In analysing the exceedingly complex influence of the external environment upon the animal, the experimenter must be able to exercise full control over all the conditions obtaining during the course of any experiment. He should therefore have at his disposal various instruments for affecting the animal by different kinds of stimuli, singly or combined, so as to imitate simple natural conditions. But we were often handicapped by the conditions in which we had to work and by the shortcomings of the instruments at our disposal, for we always found that the cerebral hemispheres were sensitive to far finer gradations of stimulus than we could furnish.

It is possible that the experimental conditions I have described may raise somewhere the objection of being abnormal and artificial. However it is hardly likely, in view of the infinite variety of stimuli met with under natural conditions, that we shall hit on one that is quite unprecedented in the life of the animal. Moreover, in dealing with any phenomenon of vast complexity it is absolutely necessary to isolate the different single factors involved, so as to study them independently, or in arbitary groups in which we can keep the individual units under control. But as a matter of fact the same objection and the same answer apply equally to the whole of animal physiology. For instance, the methods of vivisection and of the study of isolated organs and tissues, which aim at the same isolation of different individual functions, have been constantly employed, and we may safely say that the greater part of the achievements of physiology are due to the successful application of such methods of control. In our experiments it is the whole animal which is placed under a limited number of rigidly defined conditions, and only by this method is it possible to study the reflexes independently of one another.

The foregoing remarks give an idea of our general aim and of the technical side of our methods. I propose to introduce you to the first and most elementary principles of the subject matter of our research by means of a few demonstrations:

DEMONSTRATION. The dog used in the following experiment has been operated upon as described previously. It can be seen that so long as no special stimulus is applied the salivary glands remain quite inactive. But when the sounds from a beating metronome are allowed to fall upon the ear, a salivary secretion begins after 9 seconds, and in the course of 45 seconds eleven drops have been secreted. The activity of the salivary gland has thus been called into play by impulses of sound—a stimulus quite alien to food. This activity of the salivary gland cannot be regarded as anything else than a component of the alimentary reflex. Besides the secretory, the motor component of the food reflex is also very apparent in experiments of this kind. In this very experiment the dog turns in the direction from which it has been customary to present the food and begins to lick its lips vigorously.

This experiment is an example of a central nervous activity depending on the integrity of the hemispheres. A decerebrate dog would never have responded by salivary secretion to any stimulus of the kind. It is obvious also that the underlying principle of this activity is signalization. The sound of the metronome is the signal for food, and the animal reacts to the signal in the same way as if it were food; no distinction can be observed between the effects produced on the animal by the sounds of the beating metronome and showing it real food.

DEMONSTRATION. Food is shown to the animal. The salivary secretion begins after 5 seconds, and six drops are collected in the course of 15 seconds. The effect is the same as that observed with the sounds of the metronome. It is again a case of signalization, and is due to the activity of the hemispheres.

That the effect of sight and smell of food is not due to an inborn reflex, but to a reflex which has been acquired in the course of the animal's own individual existence, was shown by experiments carried out by Dr. Zitovich in the laboratory of the late Prof. Vartanov. Dr. Zitovich took several young puppies away from their mother and fed them for a considerable time only on milk. When the puppies were a few months old he established fistulae of their salivary ducts, and was thus able to measure accurately the secretory activity of the glands. He now showed these puppies some solid food—bread or meat—but no secretion of saliva was evoked. It is evident, therefore, that the sight of food does not in itself act as a direct stimulus to salivary secretion. Only after the puppies have been allowed to eat bread and meat on several occasions does the sight or smell of these foodstuffs evoke the secretion.

The following experiment serves to illustrate the activity of the salivary gland as an inborn reflex in contrast to signalization:

DEMONSTRATION. Food is suddenly introduced into the dog's mouth; secretion begins in 1 to 2 seconds. The secretion is brought about by the physical and chemical properties of the food itself acting upon receptors in the mucous membrane of the mouth and tongue. It is purely reflex.

This comparatively simple experiment explains how a decerebrate dog can die of starvation in the midst of plenty, for it will only start eating if food chances to come into contact with its mouth or tongue. Moreover, the elementary nature of the inborn reflexes, with their limitations and inadequacy, are clearly brought out in these experiments, and we are now able to appreciate the fundamental importance of those stimuli which have the character of *signals*.

Our next step will be to consider the question of the nature of signalization and of its mechanism from a purely physiological point of view. It has been mentioned already that a reflex is an inevitable reaction of the organism to an external stimulus, brought about along a definite path in the nervous system. Now it is quite evident that in signalization all the properties of a reflex are present. In the first place an external stimulus is required. This was given in our first experiment by the sounds of a metronome. These sounds falling on the auditory receptor of the dog caused the propagation of an impulse along the auditory nerve. In the brain the impulse was transmitted to the secretory nerves of the salivary glands, and passed thence to the glands, exciting them to active secretion. It is true that in the experiment with the metronome an interval of several seconds elapsed between the beginning of the stimulus and the beginning of the salivary secretion, whereas the time interval for the inborn reflex secretion was only 1 to 2 seconds. The longer latent period was, however, due to some special conditions of the experiment, as will come out more clearly as we proceed. But generally speaking the reaction to signals under natural conditions is as speedy as are the inborn reflexes. We shall be considering the latent period of signalization in fuller detail in a further lecture.

In our general survey we characterized a reflex as a necessary reaction following upon a strictly definite stimulus under strictly defined conditions. Such a definition holds perfectly true also for signalization; the only difference is that the type of the effective reaction to signals depends upon a greater number of conditions. But this does not make signalization differ fundamentally from the better known reflexes in any respect, since in the latter, variations in character or force, inhibition and absence of reflexes, can also be traced to some definite change in the conditions of the experiment.

Thorough investigation of the subject shows that accident plays no part whatever in the signalizing activity of the hemispheres, and all experiments proceed strictly according to plan. In the special laboratory I have described, the animal can frequently be kept under rigid experimental observation for 1 to 2 hours without a single drop of saliva being secreted independently of stimuli applied by the observer, although in the ordinary type of physiological laboratory experiments are very often distorted by the interference of extraneous and uncontrolled stimuli.

All these conditions leave no grounds for regarding the phenomena which we have termed "signalization" as being anything else than reflex. There is, however, another aspect of the question which at a first glance seems to point to an essential difference between the better known reflexes and signalization. Food, through its chemical and physical properties, evokes the salivary reflex in every dog right from birth, whereas this new type claimed as reflex—"the signal reflex"—is built up gradually in the course of the animal's own individual existence. But can this be considered as a fundamental point of difference, and can it hold as a valid argument against employing the term "reflex" for this new group of phenomena? It is certainly a sufficient argument for making a definite distinction between the two types of reflex and for considering the signal reflex in a group distinct from the inborn reflex. But this does not invalidate in any way our right logically to term both "reflex," since the point of distinction does not concern the character of the response on the part of the organism, but only the mode of formation of the reflex mechanism. We may take the telephonic installation as an illustration. Communication can be effected in two ways. My residence may be connected directly with the laboratory by a private line, and I may call up the laboratory whenever it pleases me to do so; or on the other hand, a connection may have to be made through the central exchange. But the result in both cases is the same. The only point of distinction between the methods is that the private line provides a permanent and readily available cable, while the other line necessitates a preliminary central connection being established. In the one case the communicating wire is always complete, in the other case a small addition must be made to the wire at the central exchange. We have a similar state of affairs in reflex action. The path of the inborn reflex is already completed at birth; but the path of the signalizing reflex has still to be completed in the higher nervous centres. We are thus brought to consider the mode of formation of new reflex mechanisms. A new reflex is formed inevitably under a given set of physiological conditions, and with the greatest ease, so that there is no need to take the subjective states of the dog into consideration. With a complete understanding of all the factors involved, the new signalizing reflexes are under the absolute control of the experimenter; they proceed according to as rigid laws as do any other physiological processes, and must be regarded as being in every sense a part of the physiological activity of living beings. I have termed this new group of reflexes conditioned reflexes to distinguish them from the inborn or unconditioned reflexes. The term "conditioned" is becoming more and more generally employed, and I think its use is fully justified in that, compared with the inborn reflexes, these new reflexes actually do depend on very many conditions, both in their formation and in the maintenance of their physiological activity. Of course the terms "conditioned" and "unconditioned" could be replaced by others of arguably equal merit. Thus, for example, we might retain the term "inborn reflexes," and call the new type "acquired reflexes"; or call the former "species reflexes" since they are characteristic of the species, and the latter "individual reflexes" since they vary from animal to animal in a species, and even in the same animal at different times and under different conditions. Or again we might call the former "conduction reflexes" and the latter "connection reflexes."

There should be no theoretical objection to the hypothesis of the formation of new physiological paths and new connections within the cerebral hemispheres. Since the especial function of the central nervous system is to establish most complicated and delicate correspondences between the organism and its environment we may not unnaturally expect to find there, on the analogy of the methods used by the technician in everyday experience, a highly developed connector system superimposed on a conductor system. The physiologist certainly should not object to this conception seeing that he has been used to employing the German conception of "Bahnung," which means a laying down of fresh physiological paths in the centres. Conditioned reflexes are phenomena of common and widespread occurrence: their establishment is an integral function in every day life. We recognize them in ourselves and in other people or animals under such names as "education," "habits," and "training"; and all of these are really nothing more than the results of an establishment of new nervous connections during the post-natal existence of the organism. They are, in actual fact, links connecting definite extraneous stimuli with their definite responsive reactions. I believe that the recognition and the study of the conditioned reflex will throw open the door to a true physiological investigation probably of all the highest nervous activities of the cerebral hemispheres, and the purpose of the present lectures is to give some account of what we have already accomplished in this direction.

We come now to consider the precise conditions under which new conditioned reflexes or new connections of nervous paths are established. The fundamental requisite is that any external stimulus which is to become the signal in a conditioned reflex must overlap in point of time with the action of an unconditioned stimulus. In the experiment which I chose as my example the unconditioned stimulus was food. Now if the intake of food by the animal takes place simultaneously with the action of a neutral stimulus which has been hitherto in no way related to food, the neutral stimulus readily acquires the property of eliciting the same reaction in the animal as would food itself. This was the case with the dog employed in our experiment with the metronome. On several occasions this animal had been stimulated by the sound of the metronome and immediately presented with food—that is, a stimulus which was neutral of itself had been superimposed upon the action of the inborn alimentary reflex. We observed that, after several repetitions of the combined stimulation, the sounds from the metronome had acquired the property of stimulating salivary secretion and of evoking the motor reactions characteristic of the alimentary reflex. The first demonstration was nothing but an example of such a conditioned stimulus in action. Precisely the same occurs with the mild defence reflex to rejectable substances. Introduction into the dog's mouth of a little of an acid solution brings about a quite definite responsive reaction. The animal sets about getting rid of the acid, shaking its head violently, opening its mouth and making movements with its tongue. At the same time it produces a copious salivary secretion. The same reaction will infallibly be obtained from any stimulus which has previously been applied a sufficient number of times while acid was being introduced into the dog's mouth. Hence a first and most essential requisite for the formation of a new conditioned reflex lies in a coincidence in time of the action of any previously neutral stimulus with some definite unconditioned stimulus. Further, it is not enough that there should be overlapping between the two stimuli; it is also and equally necessary that the conditioned stimulus should begin to operate before the unconditioned stimulus comes into action.

If this order is reversed, the unconditioned stimulus being applied first and the neutral stimulus second, the conditioned reflex cannot be established at all. Dr. Krestovnikov performed these experiments with many different modifications and controls, but the effect was always the same. The following are some of his results:

In one case 427 applications were made in succession of the odour of vanillin together with the introduction of acid into the dog's mouth, but the acid was always made to precede the vanillin by some 5 to 10 seconds. Vanillin failed to acquire the properties of a conditioned stimulus. However, in the succeeding experiment, in which the order of stimuli was reversed, the odour, this time of amyl acetate, became an effective conditioned stimulus after only 20 combinations. With another dog the loud buzzing of an electric bell set going 5 to 10 seconds after administration of food failed to establish a conditioned alimentary reflex even after 374 combinations, whereas the regular rotation of an object in front of the eyes of the animal, the rotation beginning before the administration of food, acquired the properties of a conditioned stimulus after only 5 combinations. The electric buzzer set going before the administration of food established a conditioned alimentary reflex after only a single combination.

Dr. Krestovnikov's experiments were carried out on five dogs, and the result was always negative when the neutral stimulus was applied, whether 10 seconds, 5 seconds or only a single second after the beginning of the unconditioned stimulus. During all these experiments not only the secretory reflex but also the motor reaction of the animal was carefully observed, and these observations always corroborated one another. We thus see that the first set of conditions required for the formation of a new conditioned reflex encompasses the time relation between the presentation of the unconditioned stimulus and the presentation of that agent which has to acquire the properties of a conditioned stimulus.

As regards the condition of the hemispheres themselves, an alert state of the nervous system is absolutely essential for the formation of a new conditioned reflex. If the dog is mostly drowsy during the experiments, the establishment of a conditioned reflex becomes a long and tedious process, and in extreme cases is impossible to accomplish. The hemispheres must, however, be free from any other nervous activity, and therefore in building up a new conditioned reflex it is important to avoid foreign stimuli which, falling upon the animal, would cause other reactions of their own. If this is not attended to, the establishment of a conditioned reflex is very difficult, if not impossible. Thus, for example, if the dog has been so fastened up that anything causes severe irritation, it does not matter how many times the combination of stimuli is repeated, we shall not be able to obtain a conditioned reflex. A somewhat similar case was described in the first lecture—that of the dog which exhibited the *freedom reflex* in an exaggerated degree. It can also be stated as a rule that the establishment of the first conditioned reflex in an animal is usually more difficult than the establishment of succeeding ones. It is obvious that this must be so, when we consider that even in the most favourable circumstances the experimental conditions themselves will be sure to provoke numerous different reflexes—that is, will give rise to one or other disturbing activity of the hemispheres. But this statement must be qualified by remarking that in cases where the cause of these uncontrolled reflexes is not found out, so that we are not able to get rid of them, the hemispheres themselves will help us. For if the environment of the animal during the experiment does not contain any powerful disturbing elements, then practically always the extraneous reflexes will with time gradually and spontaneously weaken in strength.

The third factor determining the facility with which new conditioned reflexes can be established is the health of the animal. A good state of health will ensure the normal functioning of the cerebral hemispheres, and we shall not have to bother with the effects of any internal pathological stimuli.

The fourth, and last, group of conditions has to do with the properties of the stimulus which is to become conditioned, and also with the properties of the unconditioned stimulus which is selected. Conditioned reflexes are quite readily formed to stimuli to which the animal is more or less indifferent at the outset, though strictly speaking no stimulus within the animal's range of perception exists to which it would be absolutely indifferent. In a normal animal the slightest alteration in the environment—even the very slightest sound or faintest odour, or the smallest change in intensity of illumination—immediately evokes the reflex which I referred to in the first lecture as the investigatory reflex—"What is it?"—manifested by a very definite motor reaction. However, if these neutral stimuli keep recurring, they spontaneously and rapidly weaken in their effect upon the hemispheres, thus bringing about bit by bit the removal of this obstacle to the establishment of a conditioned reflex. But if the extraneous stimuli are strong or unusual, the formation of a conditioned reflex will be difficult, and in extreme cases impossible.

It must also be remembered that in most cases we are not acquainted with the history of the dog before it came into the laboratory, and that we do not know what sort of conditioned reflexes have been established to stimuli which appear to be of the simplest character. But in spite of this we have, in a large number of cases, found it possible to take a strong stimulus which evoked some strong unconditioned response of its own, and still succeed in converting it into a conditioned stimulus for another reflex. Let us take for example a nocuous stimulus, such as a strong electric current or wounding or cauterization of the skin. These are obviously stimuli to vigorous unconditioned defence reflexes. The organism responds by a violent motor reaction directed towards removal of the nocuous stimulus or to its own removal from it. But we may, nevertheless, make use even of these stimuli for the establishment of a new conditioned reflex. Thus in one particular experiment a strong nocuous stimulus—an electric current of great strength—was converted into an alimentary conditioned stimulus, so that its application to the skin did not evoke the slightest defence reaction. Instead, the animal exhibited a well-marked alimentary conditioned reflex, turning its head to where it usually received the food and smacking its lips, at the same time producing a profuse secretion of saliva. The following is a record taken from a research by Dr Eroféeva:

TABLE 1

Time	Distance of Secondary Coil in Cms.	Part of Skin Stimulated	Secretion of Saliva in Drops During 30 Secs.	Motor Reaction
4.23 P.M.	4	usual place	6	In all cases the motor reaction displayed was that characteristic of an alimentary reflex; there was no slightest trace of any motor defence reflex.
4.45 "	4	" "	5	
5.7 "	2	new place	7	
5.17 "	0	" "	9	
5.45 "	0	" "	6	

Note: After each stimulation the dog was allowed to eat food for a few seconds.

Similar results were obtained from dogs in which cauterization or pricking of the skin deep enough to draw blood was made to acquire the properties of an alimentary conditioned stimulus. These experiments have been apt to upset very sensitive people; but we have been able to demonstrate, though without any pretension of penetrating into the subjective world of the dog, that they were labouring under a false impression. Subjected to the very closest scrutiny, not even the tiniest and most subtle objective phenomenon usually exhibited by animals under the influence of strong injurious stimuli can be observed in these dogs. No appreciable changes in the pulse or in the respiration occur in these animals, whereas such changes are always most prominent when the nocuous stimulus has not been converted into an alimentary conditioned stimulus. Such a remarkable phenomenon is the result of diverting the nervous impulse from one physiological path to another. This transference is dependent, however, upon a very definite condition—namely, upon the relative strengths of the two unconditioned reflexes.

Successful transformation of the unconditioned stimulus for one reflex into the conditioned stimulus for another reflex can be brought about only when the former reflex is physiologically weaker and biologically of less importance than the latter. We are led to this conclusion from a consideration of Dr. Eroféeva's experiments. A nocuous stimulus applied to the dog's skin was transformed into a conditioned stimulus for the alimentary reflex. This, we consider, was due to the fact that the alimentary reflex is in such cases stronger than the defence reflex. In the same way we all know that when dogs join in a scuffle for food they frequently sustain skin wounds, which however play no dominant part as stimuli to any defence reflex, being entirely subordinated to the reflex for food. Nevertheless there is a certain limit—there are stronger reflexes than the alimentary reflex. One is the reflex of self-preservation, of existence or non-existence, life or death. To give only one example, it was found impossible to transform a defence reaction into an alimentary conditioned reflex when the stimulus to the unconditioned defence reaction was a strong electric current applied to skin overlying bone with no muscular layer intervening. This signifies that the afferent nervous impulses set up by injury to the bone, and signalizing far greater danger than those set up by injury to the skin, cannot acquire even a temporary connection with the part of the brain from which the alimentary reflex is controlled. Nevertheless, on the whole, the foregoing considerations emphasize the advantage of using the alimentary reflex for most of our experiments, since in the hierarchy of reflexes this holds a very high place.

While, as we have seen, very strong and even specialized stimuli can under certain conditions acquire the properties of conditioned stimuli, there is, on the other hand, a minimum strength below which stimuli cannot be given conditioned properties. Thus a thermal stimulus of 45° C. applied to the skin can be made into an alimentary conditioned reflex, whereas at 38° to 39° C. (approximately 2° C. above the skin temperature in the dog) a thermal stimulus is ineffective [experiments of Dr. Solomonov]. Similarly, while with the help of a very strong unconditioned stimulus it is possible to convert a very unsuitable stimulus—for example, one which naturally evokes a different unconditioned reflex—into a conditioned stimulus, it is exceedingly difficult or even impossible with the help of only a weak unconditioned stimulus to transform even a very favourable neutral stimulus into a conditioned stimulus. Even where such a conditioned reflex is successfully established, its occurrence results only in a very small reflex response. Some unconditioned stimuli may be permanently weak, others may display a weakness which is only temporary—varying with the condition of the animal. As an example of the last we may take food. In the hungry animal food naturally brings about a powerful unconditioned reflex, and the conditioned reflex develops quickly. But in a dog which has not long been fed the unconditioned stimulus has only a small effect, and alimentary conditioned reflexes either are not formed at all or are established very slowly.

By complying with all the conditions which I have enumerated— which is not a very difficult task—a new conditioned reflex is infallibly obtained. We apply to the receptors of the animal rigidly defined stimuli; these stimuli necessarily result in the formation of a new connection in the hemispheres with a consequent development of a typical reflex reaction.

To sum up, we may legitimately claim the study of the formation and properties of conditioned reflexes as a special department of physiology. There is no reason for thinking about all these events in any other way, and it is my belief that in these questions prejudices blunt the intellect and that generally speaking the preconceptions of the human mind stand in the way of any admission that the highest physiological activity of the hemisphere is rigidly determined. The difficulty is mainly due to the tremendous complexity of our subjective states; and, of course, these cannot yet be traced to their primary causations.

[3]

Operant Conditioning

FRED S. KELLER and
WILLIAM N. SCHOENFELD

SKINNER AND OPERANT CONDITIONING

In 1930, there was published, in the Proceedings of the National Academy of Science, a short paper on the eating behavior of white rats. The author was B. F. Skinner, then a graduate student in psychology at Harvard University. Skinner described, in his paper, an experimental method that, in slightly modified form, has become a fixture in modern experimental research. It involved simply (1) a device for giving a small pellet of food to a hungry white rat each time that the animal pushed open the swinging door of a food-bin at one end of his experimental chamber; and (2) a recording mechanism that caused a vertical movement of a pen upon the paper-covered surface of a slowly revolving cylinder (a kymograph drum) whenever the rat opened the door of the bin to obtain the pellet. The vertical pen marks were made at right angles to the drum movement and were cumulative—that is, each upward distance that the pen moved was added, by a rachet device, to the preceding one. Since a short period of time was required for the eating of each pellet before the next door-opening took place, and since the drum continued to revolve steadily during this period, each mark was displaced slightly to the right of the preceding one. This provided a step-wise record, of the sort shown in Figure 1. The vertical lines (of equal length) indicate successive door-opening responses and the horizontal lines (not necessarily equal in length) indicate the time elapsing between responses. Since the pellets were of a constant size and weight (about $\frac{1}{15}$ of a gram), an *eating rate* is represented.

SOURCE: From *Principles of Psychology* by Fred S. Keller and William N. Schoenfeld. Copyright, 1950, Appleton-Century-Crofts, Inc. Reprinted by permission of Appleton-Century-Crofts.

154

The step-wise effect is very obvious in Figure 1 because of the size of the time-units and response-units we have selected. If the units had been smaller, the effect would have been less pronounced. Figure 2 is copied from an actual record obtained in Skinner's experiment. In this case, the steps are so close together that they are imperceptible in our copy and a fairly smooth *curve* of eating results.

Such a curve is characteristically obtained when a rat is fed daily with pellets at a regular time, and is deprived of food during the intervening periods. It shows that, under such a regimen, the animal begins by responding at a relatively high rate and gradually

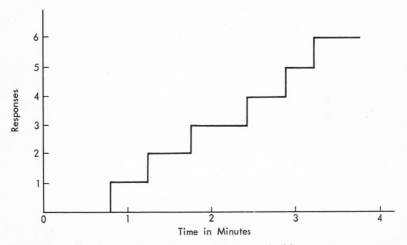

FIGURE 1. The construction of a cumulative record of bar-pressing responses. (From *Principles of Psychology* by Fred S. Keller and William N. Schoenfeld. Copyright, 1950, Appleton-Century-Crofts, Inc. Reprinted and reproduced by permission of Appleton-Century-Crofts.)

slows down as he nears the point of satiation. The curve is, to use the mathematician's term, *negatively accelerated.*

The curve does not, of course, represent *all* eating behavior in rats. Had the animals been permitted to live in the experimental box and eat whenever their hunger led them to do so, they would probably have eaten at a somewhat slower but very constant rate on each occasion: *straight-line,* rather than negatively accelerated, curves would have resulted. The important fact is the *orderliness* of the behavior that appears under a specified set of experimental conditions. The search for orderly relationships is characteristic of all science and, with the discovery of a single example, one is often led to hunt for more.

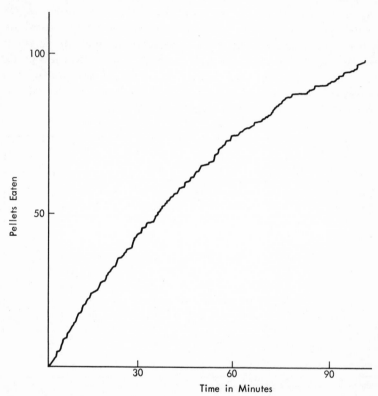

FIGURE 2. A cumulative record of a rat's food-getting responses (bar-pressing for pellets) during a daily eating period. (Reproduced from Figure 7 from *The Behavior of Organisms:* An Experimental Analysis by B. F. Skinner. Copyright, 1938, D. Appleton-Century-Company, Inc. Reprinted by permission of Appleton-Century-Crofts.)

The only behavior required of the rats in Skinner's experiment was the simple and fairly natural act of pushing open a door to reach food. How or when the animal *learned* to perform this act was not determined, but a second experiment, reported by Skinner in 1932, dealt with this question. Using a modification of his earlier apparatus, he tried to find out the way in which a new act, one not previously related to food-getting, might come to be so related. The act chosen was that of pressing downward, with a force of about ten grams, a small lever. This lever, or bar, was situated at one end of a response chamber in a sound-resistant and light-proof experimental box (see Figure 3). Its downward movement caused the ejection of a pellet of food, from a magazine in an adjoining chamber, into a small metal cup or tray. With every activation of the food-magazine by the bar depression, a record was made on a kymograph drum outside the experimental box. The record was cumulative, as in the study of eating rate.

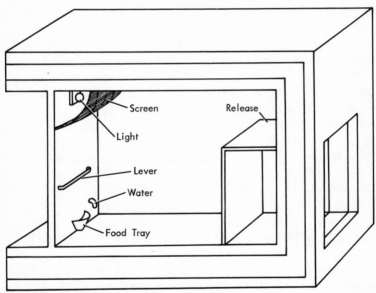

FIGURE 3. An early model of Skinner's bar-pressing apparatus. (Reproduced from Figure 8 from *The Behavior of Organisms: An Experimental Analysis* by B. F. Skinner. Copyright, 1938, D. Appleton-Century-Company, Inc. Reprinted by permission of Appleton-Century-Crofts.)

The experimental procedure involved (1) a preliminary acclimatization of the hungry animal to the response chamber, with a supply of food in the tray, until he moved and ate freely in the situation;

(2) further sessions in which the rat was accustomed to eating pellets, when they were discharged, one at a time, from the food-magazine by the experimenter; and (3) training in the bar-pressing response. Stage 3, the important one in this experiment, was conducted as follows.

After twenty-four hours' deprivation of food, the rat was placed in the response compartment of the box. The bar was present, the food-magazine was filled with pellets, and a water supply was obtainable from a small tube near the tray, but the tray itself was empty. When the rat approached the tray, as he had learned to do in stages 1 and 2, and found no food, he soon engaged in exploratory behavior of one sort or another within the chamber. In ten or fifteen minutes, often sooner, this exploration led to a depression of the bar, usually accomplished by one or both of the rat's forepaws as he raised himself to sniff at the wall above the tray or at the slots through which the bar entered the chamber. The bar-depression was accompanied by the click of the food-magazine (to which the rat was accustomed in stage 2) and the ejection of a pellet into the tray. At the same time, the response was recorded on the kymograph drum outside the box.

A second bar-pressing response usually followed soon after, in some cases immediately after, the first pellet had been seized and eaten, and the animal quickly developed a maximal rate of pressing and eating. The sample records in Figure 4 illustrate this clearly. The two lower curves in this figure show the immediate development of a maximal response rate; the upper curves show a slight *positive* acceleration at their beginning, with a few responses occurring before a constant eating rate appears.

It is clear from these curves that the rats quickly learned to press the bar when food resulted from the act. Indeed, if we were unaware of the preliminary stages of the experiment—the acclimatizing of the animal to the apparatus and the training to approach the tray when the magazine was operated—we might conclude from some of the records that the rat had already solved the bar-pressing problem when it was first presented. Except in those animals that produced positively accelerated curves, the learning process was practically instantaneous. And in no case was there anything com-

parable to the gradual and irregular progress that typified the behavior of Thorndike's cats.

Skinner called his study an experiment "On the Rate of Formation
of a Conditioned Reflex." It was obvious to him, however, that the
rat's behavior could not adequately be described in terms of the
conventional Pavlovian paradigm. A number of insurmountable
barriers stood directly in the path of such an analysis. A practical

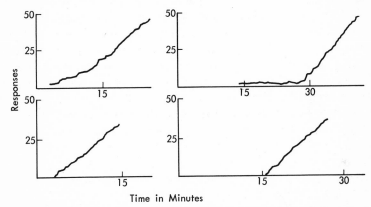

Time in Minutes

Figure 4. Some typical cumulative response curves obtained from hungry
rats on the day of conditioning a bar-pressing response for the first time. Each
response was reinforced with a pellet of food. Notice that conditioning is commonly "instantaneous," and that the response rate is usually steady. (Reproduced from Figure 9 from *The Behavior of Organisms: An Experimental
Analysis* by B. F. Skinner. Copyright, 1938, D. Appleton-Century-Company,
Inc. Reprinted by permission of Appleton-Century-Crofts.)

exercise will convince you of the difficulties in applying Pavlov's
principle to the bar-pressing situation. Construct for yourself the
paradigm, after the model in Chapter 1, labeling each S and R
appropriately to show how the reflex is established. What are the
two reflexes with which you begin? Where is the third reflex, the
conditioned one? How does the "conditioned" stimulus come to act
as a substitute for the "unconditioned" in eliciting the response to
the latter? Be sure that you limit yourself to *observable*, rather than
purely hypothetical, stimuli and responses.

As an outcome of his own struggle with this problem, Skinner
proposed, in 1935, and again in 1937, that we recognize *two* types
of conditioning: Type S and Type R. Type S is no more than the

classical Pavlovian conditioning, in which reinforcement is always related to the presentation of a *stimulus*—for example, food is given when a tone is sounded. Type R, which is represented in the acquisition of bar-pressing behavior, involves a relation between reinforcement and a specific *response*—thus, food is given when the bar is pressed.

A paradigm suitable for Type R conditioning is shown below, along with the familiar Type S schema. A comparison of the two will help you to understand some of the ways in which the two types differ.

TYPE R: s . . . . . R (bar-pressing)⟶S (food)⟶R (eating)

(The arrow in the paradigm = "is followed by.")

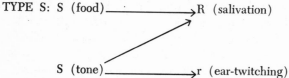

TYPE S: S (food)⟶R (salivation)

S (tone)⟶r (ear-twitching)

Type S conditioning, as we have seen, involves the *elicitation* of a response (salivation) by an identifiable conditioned stimulus (tone) that is under the experimenter's control. In Type R conditioning, the specific stimulus that initially evokes the response (bar-pressing) *cannot* be identified. This is indicated by the small *s* of the Type R paradigm. We need not assume that bar-pressing has no cause or that it can bear no relation to environmental stimuli; we shall see, in Chapter 5, that stimuli may "set the occasion" for this response. But, for all practical purposes, the response just *occurs*, is initially *emitted*, without relation to any specifiable stimulus agency.

Type S conditioning involves *stimulus substitution* and the formation of a *new reflex*. The tone, in our example, comes to act as a substitute for food in eliciting salivation; and tone-salivation is the new reflex. In Type R conditioning, however, there is merely the strengthening of a reflex that already exists in the organism's repertory. Bar-pressing, for instance, occurs with *some* frequency prior to any reinforcement with food. At any rate, no substitution is involved and no new stimulus-response relation is formed.

Type S conditioning *prepares* the organism for reinforcement. The tone comes to elicit salivation in advance of the food, paving the way, as it were, for its digestion. Type R conditioning *procures* or *produces* the reinforcement—bar-pressing provides the rat with a food pellet. The two processes may take place concurrently, although our observation is usually limited to one of them. Pavlov himself noted that Type S conditioning was commonly accompanied by "motor reactions" of head-turning and the like which we would now ascribe to the development of a Type R conditioning. More recently, another investigator (Brogden, 1939b) has shown that when dogs are reinforced with food for making a leg movement (Type R conditioning) in the presence of a tone, there is the simultaneous development of conditioned (Type S) salivation.

With respect to this last distinction, a simple example may not be superfluous. A hungry boy, home from school, is met at the door with the odor of freshly baked cookies. In accordance with his history of Type S conditioning, his "mouth waters," preparing him for what may follow. But *nothing* will follow unless he has been conditioned in Type R fashion to make his way to the kitchen and exhibit the verbal or other behavior which, in the past, has been productive of cookies.

THE LAW OF OPERANT CONDITIONING

These differences between Type S and Type R conditioning are associated with a broader distinction, mentioned briefly in the preceding chapter, between two fundamental classes of behavior. One of these, which includes all those responses, conditioned or unconditioned, that are *elicited* by known stimuli, we called *respondent*. The other class, comprising all those responses that are *emitted* more or less independently of identifiable stimuli, we may now call *operant*. The spontaneous movements of an infant organism, human or otherwise, are mainly of the latter type; and so are the "voluntary" acts of human beings. In fact, most of our behavior in the routine affairs of everyday life is clearly operant, in that it *operates* or acts upon the environment to produce the satisfaction of our basic needs. Respondent behavior is much less commonly observed and seldom, if ever, operates upon the environment to produce anything.

Operant behavior is conditioned primarily, if not exclusively, in Type R fashion; respondent behavior is usually conditioned in Type S fashion. Hence, when it suits our convenience, we may speak of Type R as operant conditioning, in the same way that we speak of Type S as respondent. Again, just as we refer to any single example of respondent behavior as *a* respondent, we shall refer to each example of operant behavior as *an* operant.

We have seen, in Chapter 2, that the *strength* of a respondent is commonly measured in terms of latency and response magnitude. Neither of these measures is satisfactory in determining the strength of an operant. Latency can have no meaning in the absence of an identifiable stimulus from which to measure the S-R interval; and the magnitude of an operant response does not change during conditioning in the orderly manner that typifies the respondent. The amount of saliva secreted by a dog in response to a tone may increase gradually with successive tone-food combinations, but the force of a bar-pressing response may be as great on its first appearance as it is on its fifty-first, and it may fluctuate throughout a long series of emissions.

Our best measure of operant strength is *frequency of occurrence*. An operant is strong when emitted often within a given period of time; it is weak when emitted rarely. We have, in a sense, assumed this already, in the case of bar-pressing: a steady, high rate of responding implied a strong response-tendency, whereas a slow, uneven rate implied a weak one. In the case of a respondent, frequency is a useless measure—in fact, no measure at all—since the response rate is determined solely by the rate at which the eliciting stimulus is presented to the organism.

"If the occurrence of an operant is followed by the presentation of a reinforcing stimulus, the strength is increased" (Skinner, 1938). We can now begin to grasp the significance of this statement of the principle of Type R conditioning. Bar-pressing is an operant. It occurs with a certain low frequency prior to any experimental procedures that we may apply. Its strength is increased when it is followed by reinforcement. Increased strength means merely that it occurs with higher frequency than it did before.

TABLE 1

Comparison Between Type S and Type R Conditioning

Type S	*Type R*
Paradigm: $$S_1 \rightarrow R_2$$ $$\nearrow$$ $$S_2 \ldots r_2$$	Paradigm: $s \ldots \ldots R \rightarrow S$ (reinforcement)
Response is elicited.	Response is emitted.
Stimulus substitution.	No substitution of stimuli.
Formation of new reflex.	Strengthening of reflex already in repertory.
"Preparation" by conditioned stimulus for the unconditioned reinforcement that follows. The response does not manipulate the environment.	Response "procures" the reinforcement. The response "operates" on the environment.
Commonly, if not always, is mediated by the autonomic nervous system, involving smooth muscles and glands.	Mediated by somatic nervous system, involving skeletal muscles.
Usually measured in terms of reflex latency or magnitude.	Usually measured in terms of reflex rate; sometimes, latency.

OPERANT CONDITIONING AND THE LAW OF EFFECT

When you compare the work of Skinner with that of Thorndike, you may be impressed by the numerous dissimilarities. The two men used different species of animals, different apparatus, and different experimental procedures. Yet, when you consider that both situations required a manipulation of some environmental object; when you note that the presentation of food was in each case contingent upon this manipulation; and when you compare the principle of Type R conditioning with the law of effect, you may notice a striking agreement. Both formulations emphasize the influence of the outcome of a response upon its strength: Thorndike calls it "satisfaction" and Skinner speaks of a "reinforcing stimulus." Skinner's formula seems to be the narrower of the two, since it contains no equivalent of Thorndike's "discomfort," yet Thorndike himself later came to discount the weakening effect of discomfort—a point to which we shall return later.

There is still another similarity. In spite of Thorndike's emphasis upon a connection or bond between situation and response, it is perfectly clear that he does not refer to the Pavlovian type of connection. He would have been the last to suggest that the loop-pulling or other manipulative behavior of his cats was elicited in the same way that food elicits salivation, a shock elicits foot-withdrawal, or a cinder in the eye elicits tears.

This last point requires some elaboration. Throughout much of the present chapter, we have underlined the fact that a large proportion of an organism's behavior is emitted rather than elicited, and is conditioned in Type R rather than Type S fashion. We may have led you to think that responses like loop-pulling and bar-pressing can have no relation whatever to stimuli. If such was your impression, it should be corrected. Operant behavior, however spontaneous in its initial occurrence, very soon becomes associated with stimuli. The cat that has learned to pull the loop, or the rat that has learned to press the bar, reacts to stimuli or stimulus combinations, even if we cannot specify them completely. In the absence of a loop or bar, the animal seldom paws the air. But these stimuli are *not* eliciting: they are not related to their responses in the same way that salivation is related to food or foot-withdrawal is related to electric shock. It is just that the responses are *more likely to occur* in the presence of such objects. To use an expression quoted earlier, these stimuli *set the occasion* for responses. Later on, when we consider this matter in more detail, we shall refer to them as *discriminative* stimuli.

[4]

The Taming of the Shrew

KONRAD Z. LORENZ

> Though Nature, red in tooth and claw,
> With ravine, shrieked against his creed.
> TENNYSON, *In Memoriam*

All shrews are particularly difficult to keep; this is not because, as we are led proverbially to believe, they are hard to tame, but because the metabolism of these smallest of mammals is so very fast that they will die of hunger within two or three hours if the food supply fails. Since they feed exclusively on small, living animals, mostly insects, and demand, of these, considerably more than their own weight every day, they are most exacting charges. At the time of which I am writing, I had never succeeded in keeping any of the terrestrial shrews alive for any length of time; most of those that I happened to obtain had probably only been caught because they were already ill and they died almost at once. I had never succeeded in procuring a healthy specimen. Now the order Insectivora is very low in the genealogical hierarchy of mammals and is, therefore, of particular interest to the comparative ethologist. Of the whole group, there was only one representative with whose behaviour I was tolerably familiar, namely the hedgehog, an extremely interesting animal of whose ethology Professor Herter of Berlin has made a very thorough study. Of the behaviour of all other members of the family practically nothing is known. Since they are nocturnal and partly subterranean animals, it is nearly impossible to approach them in field observation, and the difficulty of keeping them in captivity had hitherto precluded their study in the laboratory. So the Insectivores were officially placed on my programme.

SOURCE: *King Solomon's Ring* by Konrad Z. Lorenz. Copyright © 1952 by Thomas Y. Crowell Company, New York, publishers, and reprinted with their permission. Also reprinted by permission of Methuen & Co. Ltd., London and Konrad Z. Lorenz.

165

First I tried to keep the common mole. It was easy to procure a healthy specimen, caught to order in the nursery gardens of my father-in-law, and I found no difficulty in keeping it alive. Immediately on its arrival, it devoured an almost incredible quantity of earthworms which, from the very first moment, it took from my hand. But, as an object of behaviour study, it proved most disappointing. Certainly, it was interesting to watch its method of disappearing in the space of a few seconds under the surface of the ground, to study its astoundingly efficient use of its strong, spade-shaped forepaws, and to feel their amazing strength when one held the little beast in one's hand. And again, it was remarkable with what surprising exactitude it located, by smell, from underground, the earthworms which I put on the surface of the soil in its terrarium. But these observations were the only benefits I derived from it. It never became any tamer and it never remained above ground any longer than it took to devour its prey; after this, it sank into the earth as a submarine sinks into the water. I soon grew tired of procuring the immense quantities of living food it required and, after a few weeks, I set it free in the garden.

It was years afterwards, on an excursion to that extraordinary lake, the Neusiedlersee, which lies on the Hungarian border of Austria, that I again thought of keeping an insectivore. This large stretch of water, though not thirty miles from Vienna, is an example of the peculiar type of lake found in the open steppes of Eastern Europe and Asia. More than thirty miles long and half as broad, its deepest parts are only about five feet deep and it is much shallower on the average. Nearly half its surface is overgrown with reeds which form an ideal habitat for all kinds of water-birds. Great colonies of white, purple, and grey heron and spoonbills live among the reeds and, until a short while ago, glossy ibis were still to be found here. Greylag geese breed here in great numbers and, on the eastern, reedless shore, avocets and many other rare waders can regularly be found. On the occasion of which I am speaking, we, a dozen tired zoologists, under the experienced guidance of my friend Otto Koenig, were wending our way, slowly and painfully, through the forest of reeds. We were walking in single file, Koenig first, I second, with a few students in our wake. We literally left a wake, an inky-black one in pale grey water. In the reed-forests of Lake Neusiedel, you walk knee deep in slimy, black ooze, wonderfully perfumed by sulphuretted-hydrogen-producing bacteria. This mud clings tenaciously and only releases its hold on your foot with a loud, protesting plop at every step.

After a few hours of this kind of wading you discover aching muscles whose very existence you had never suspected. From the knees to the hips you are immersed in the milky, clay-coloured water characteristic of the lake, which, among the reeds, is populated by myriads of extremely hungry leeches conforming to the old pharmaceutical recipe, *Hirudines medicinales maxime affamati*. The rest of your person inhabits the upper air, which here consists of clouds of tiny mosquitoes whose bloodthirsty attacks are all the more exasperating because you require both your hands to part the dense reeds in front of you and can only slap your face at intervals. The British ornithologist who may perhaps have envied us some of our rare specimens will perceive that bird-watching on Lake Neusiedel is not, after all, an entirely enviable occupation.

We were thus wending our painful way through the rushes when suddenly Koenig stopped and pointed mutely towards a pond, free from reeds, that stretched in front of us. At first, I could only see whitish water, dark blue sky and green reeds, the standard colors of Lake Neusiedel. Then, suddenly, like a cork popping up on to the surface, there appeared, in the middle of the pool, a tiny black animal, hardly bigger than a man's thumb. And for a moment I was in the rare position of a zoologist who sees a specimen and is not able to classify it, in the literal sense of the word: I did not know to which class of vertebrates the object of my gaze belonged. For the first fraction of a second I took it for the young of some diving bird of a species unknown to me. It appeared to have a beak and it swam on the water like a bird, not in it as a mammal. It swam about in narrow curves and circles, very much like a whirligig beetle, creating an extensive wedge-shaped wake, quite out of proportion to the tiny animal's size. Then a second little beast popped up from below, chased the first one with a shrill, bat-like twitter, then both dived and were gone. The whole episode had not lasted five seconds.

I stood open-mouthed, my mind racing. Koenig turned round with a broad grin, calmly detached a leech that was sticking like a leech to his wrist, wiped away the trickle of blood from the wound, slapped his cheek, thereby killing thirty-five mosquitoes, and asked, in the tone of an examiner, "What was that?" I answered as calmly as I could, "water-shrews," thanking, in my heart, the leech and the mosquitoes for the respite they had given me to collect my thoughts. But my mind was racing on: water-shrews ate fishes and frogs which were easy to procure in any quantity; water-shrews were less subterranean than most other insectivores; they were the very insectivores to keep in captivity. "That's an animal I must catch and keep"; I said to my friend. "That is easy," he responded. "There is a nest with young under the floor mat of my tent." I had slept that night in this tent and Koenig had not thought it worth while to tell me of the shrews; such things are, to him, as much a matter of course as wild little spotted crakes feeding out of his hand, or as any other wonders of his queer kingdom in the reeds.

On our return to the tent that evening, he showed me the nest. It contained eight young which, compared with their mother, who rushed away as we lifted the mat, were of enormous size. They were considerably more than half her length and must each have weighed well between a fourth and a third of their dam: that is to say, the whole litter weighed, at a very modest estimate, twice as much as the old shrew. Yet they were still quite blind and the tips of their teeth were only just visible in their rosy mouths. And two days later when I took them under my care, they were still quite unable to eat even the soft abdomens of grasshoppers, and in spite of evident greed, they chewed interminably on a soft piece of frog's meat without succeeding in detaching a morsel from it. On our journey home, I fed them on the squeezed-out insides of grasshoppers and finely minced frog's meat, a diet on which they obviously throve. Arrived home in Altenberg, I improved on this diet by preparing a food from the squeezed-out insides of mealworm larvae, with some finely chopped small, fresh fishes, worked into a sort of gravy with a little milk. They consumed large quantities of this food, and their little nest-box looked quite small in comparison with the big china bowl whose contents they emptied three times a day. All these observations raise the problem of how the female water-shrew succeeds in feeding her gigantic litter. It is absolutely impossible that she should do so on milk alone. Even on a more concentrated diet my young shrews devoured the equivalent of their own weight daily and this meant nearly twice the weight of a grown shrew. Yet, at that time of their lives, young shrews could not possibly engulf a frog or a fish brought whole to them by their mother, as my charges indisputably proved. I can only think that the mother feeds her young by regurgitation of chewed food. Even thus, it is little short of miraculous that the adult female should be able to obtain enough meat to sustain herself and her voracious progeny.

When I brought them home, my young water-shrews were still blind. They had not suffered from the journey and were as sleek and fat as one could wish. Their black, glossy coats were reminiscent of moles, but the white colour of their underside, as well as the round, streamlined contours of their bodies reminded me distinctly of penguins, and not, indeed, without justification: both the streamlined form and the light underside are adaptations to a life in the water. Many free-swimming animals, mammals, birds, amphibians and fishes, are silvery-white below in order to be invisible to enemies swimming in the depths. Seen from below, the shining white belly blends perfectly with the reflecting surface film of the water. It is very characteristic of these water animals that the dark dorsal and the white ventral colours do not merge gradually into each other as is the case in "counter-shaded" land animals whose colouring is calculated to make them invisible by eliminating the contrasting shade on their undersides. As in the killer whale, in dolphins, and in penguins, the white underside of the water-shrew is divided from the dark upper side by a sharp line which runs, often in very decorative curves, along the animal's flank. Curiously enough, this border-line between black and white showed considerable variations in individuals and even on both sides of one animal's body. I welcomed this, since it enabled me to recognize my shrews personally.

Three days after their arrival in Altenberg my eight shrew babies opened their eyes and began, very cautiously, to explore the precincts of their nest-box. It was now time to remove them to an appropriate container, and on this question I expended much hard thinking. The enormous quantity of food they consumed and, consequently, of excrement they produced, made it impossible to keep them in an ordinary aquarium whose water, within a day, would have become a stinking brew. Adequate sanitation was imperative for particular reasons; in ducks, grebes and all water-fowl, the plumage must be kept perfectly dry if the animal is to remain in a state of health, and the same premise may reasonably be expected to hold good of the shrew's fur. Now water which has been polluted soon turns strongly alkaline and this I knew to be very bad for the plumage of water-birds. It causes saponification of the fat to which the feathers owe their waterproof quality, and the bird becomes thoroughly wet and is unable to stay on the water. I hold the record, as far as I know hitherto unbroken by any other bird-lover, for having kept dabchicks alive and healthy in captivity for nearly two years, and even then they did not die but escaped, and may still be living. My experience with these birds proved the absolute necessity of keeping the water perfectly clean; whenever it became a little dirty I noticed their feathers beginning to get wet, a danger which they anxiously tried to counteract by constantly preening themselves. I had, therefore, to keep these little grebes in crystal-clear water which was changed every day, and I rightly assumed that the same would be necessary for my water-shrews.

I took a large aquarium tank, rather over a yard in length and about two feet wide. At each end of this, I placed two little tables, and weighted them down with heavy stones so that they would not float. Then I filled up the tank until the water was level with the tops of the tables. I did not at first push the tables close against the panes of the tank, which was rather narrow, for fear that the shrews might become trapped under water in the blind alley beneath a table and drown there; this precaution, however, subsequently proved unnecessary. The water-shrew which, in its natural state, swims great distances under the ice, is quite able to find its way to the open surface in much more difficult situations. The nest-box, which was placed on one of the tables, was equipped with a sliding shutter, so that I could imprison the shrews whenever the container had to be cleaned. In the morning, at the hour of general cage-cleaning, the shrews were usually at home and asleep, so that the procedure caused them no appreciable disturbance. I will admit that I take great pride in devising, by creative imagination, suitable containers for animals of which nobody, myself included, has had any previous experience, and it was particularly gratifying that the contraption described above proved so satisfactory that I never had to alter even the minutest detail.

When first my baby shrews were liberated in this container they took a very long time to explore the top of the table on which their nest-box was standing. The water's edge seemed to exert a strong attraction; they approached it ever and again, smelled the surface and seemed to feel along it with the long, fine whiskers which surround their pointed snouts like a halo and represent not only their most important organ of touch but the most important of all their sensory organs. Like other aquatic mammals, the water shrew differs from the terrestrial members of its class in that its nose, the guiding organ of the average mammal, is of no use whatsoever in its under-water hunting. The water-shrew's whiskers are actively mobile like the antennae of an insect or the fingers of a blind man.

Exactly as mice and many other small rodents would do under similar conditions, the shrews interrupted their careful exploration of their new surroundings every few minutes to dash wildly back into the safe cover of their nest-box. The survival value of this peculiar behaviour is evident: the animal makes sure, from time to time that it has not lost its way and that it can, at a moment's notice, retreat to the one place it knows to be safe. It was a queer spectacle to see those podgy black figures slowly and carefully whiskering their way forward and, in the next second, with lightning speed, dash back to the nest-box. Queerly enough, they did not run straight through the little door, as one would have expected, but in their wild dash for safety they jumped, one and all, first on to the roof of the box and only then, whiskering along its edge, found the opening and slipped in with a half somersault, their back turned nearly vertically downward. After many repetitions of this manoeuvre, they were able to find the opening without feeling for it; they "knew" perfectly its whereabouts yet still persisted in the leap on to the roof. They jumped on to it and immediately vaulted in through the door, but they never, as long as they lived, found out that the leap and vault which had become their habit was really quite unnecessary and that they could have run in directly without this extraordinary detour. We shall hear more about this dominance of path habits in the water-shrew presently.

It was only on the third day, when the shrews had become thoroughly acquainted with the geography of their little rectangular island, that the largest and most enterprising of them ventured into the water. As is so often the case with mammals, birds, reptiles and fishes, it was the largest and most handsomely coloured male which played the role of leader. First he sat on the edge of the water and thrust in the fore part of his body, at the same time frantically paddling with his fore-legs but still clinging with his hind ones to the board. Then he slid in, but in the next moment took fright, scampered madly across the surface very much after the manner of a frightened duckling, and jumped out on to the board at the opposite end of the tank. There he sat, excitedly grooming his belly with one hind paw, exactly as coypu and beavers do. Soon he quietened down and sat still for a moment. Then he went to the water's edge a second time, hesitated for a moment, and plunged in; diving immediately, he swam ecstatically about under water, swerving upward and downward again, running quickly along the bottom, and finally jumping out of the water at the same place as he had first entered it.

When I first saw a water-shrew swimming I was most struck by a thing which I ought to have expected but did not: at the moment of diving, the little black and white beast appears to be made of silver. Like the plumage of ducks and grebes, but quite unlike the fur of most water mammals, such as seals, otters, beavers or coypus, the fur of the water-shrew remains absolutely dry under water, that is to say, it retains a thick layer of air while the animal is below the surface. In the other mammals mentioned above, it is only the short, wooly undercoat that remains dry, the superficial hair-tips becoming wet, wherefore the animal looks its natural colour when under water and is superficially wet when it emerges. I was already aware of the peculiar qualities of the waterproof fur of the shrew, and, had I given it a thought, I should have known that it would look, under water, exactly like the air-retaining fur on the underside of a water beetle or on the abdomen of a water spider. Nevertheless the wonderful, transparent silver coat of the shrew was, to me, one of those delicious surprises that nature has in store for her admirers.

Another surprising detail which I only noticed when I saw my shrews in the water was that they have a fringe of stiff, erectile hairs on the outer side of their fifth toes and on the underside of their tails. These form collapsible oars and a collapsible rudder. Folded and inconspicuous as long as the animal is on dry land, they unfold the moment it enters the water and broaden the effective surface of the propelling feet and of the steering tail by a considerable area.

Like penguins, the water-shrews looked rather awkward and ungainly on dry land but were transformed into objects of elegance and grace on entering the water. As long as they walked, their strongly convex underside made them look pot-bellied and reminiscent of an old, overfed dachshund. But under water, the very same protruding belly balanced harmoniously the curve of their back and gave a beautifully symmetrical streamline which, together with their silver coating and the elegance of their movements, made them a sight of entrancing beauty.

When they had all become familiar with the water, their container was one of the chief attractions that our research station had to offer to any visiting naturalists or animal-lovers. Unlike all other mammals of their size, the water-shrews were largely diurnal and, except in the early hours of the morning, three or four of them were constantly on the scene. It was exceedingly interesting to watch their movements upon and under the water. Like the whirligig beetle, Gyrinus, they could turn in an extremely small radius without diminishing their speed, a faculty for which the large rudder surface of the tail with its fringe of erectile hairs is evidently essential. They had two different ways of diving, either by taking a little jump as grebes or coots do and working their way down at a steep angle, or by simply lowering their snout under the surface and paddling very fast till they reached "planing speed," thus working their way downward on the principle of the inclined plane—in other words, performing the converse movement of an ascending aeroplane. The water-shrew must expend a large amount of energy in staying down, since the air contained in its fur exerts a strong pull upwards. Unless it is paddling straight downwards, a thing it rarely does, it is forced to maintain a constant minimum speed, keeping its body at a slightly downward angle, in order not to float to the surface. While swimming under water the shrew seems to flatten, broadening its body in a peculiar fashion, in order to present a better planing surface to the water. I never saw my shrews try to cling by their claws to any under-water objects, as the dipper is alleged to do. When they seemed to be running along the bottom, they were really swimming close above it, but perhaps the smooth gravel on the bottom of the tank was unsuitable for holding on to and it did not occur to me then to offer them a rougher surface. They were very playful when in the water and chased one another loudly twittering on the surface, or silently in the depths. Unlike any other mammal, but just like water birds, they could rest on the surface; this they used to do, rolling partly over and grooming themselves. Once out again, they instantly proceeded to clean their fur—one is almost tempted to say "preen" it, so similar was their behaviour to that of ducks which have just left the water after a long swim.

Most interesting of all was their method of hunting under water. They came swimming along with an erratic course, darting a foot or so forward very swiftly in a straight line, then starting to gyrate in looped turns at reduced speed. While swimming straight and swiftly their whiskers were, as far as I could see, laid flat against their head, but while circling they were erect and bristled out in all directions, as they sought contact with some prey. I have no reason to believe that vision plays any part in the water-shrew's hunting, except perhaps in the activation of its tactile search. My shrews may have noticed visually the presence of the live tadpoles or little fishes which I put in the tank, but in the actual hunting of its prey the animal is exclusively guided by its sense of touch, located in the wide-spreading whiskers on its snout. Certain small free-swimming species of cat-fish find their prey by exactly the same method. When these fishes swim fast and straight, the long feelers on their snout are depressed but, like the shrew's whiskers, are stiffly spread out when the fish becomes conscious of the proximity of potential prey; like the shrew, the fish then begins to gyrate blindly in order to establish contact with its prey. It may not even be necessary for the water-shrew actually to touch its prey with one of its whiskers. Perhaps, at very close range, the water vibration caused by the movements of a small fish, a tadpole or a water-insect is perceptible by those sensitive tactile organs. It is quite impossible to determine this question by mere observation, for the action is much too quick for the human eye. There is a quick turn and a snap and the shrew is already paddling shorewards with a wriggling creature in its maw.

In relation to its size, the water-shrew is perhaps the most terrible predator of all vertebrate animals, and it can even vie with the invertebrates, including the murderous Dytiscus larva described in the third chapter of this book. It has been reported by A. E. Brehm that water-shrews have killed fish more than sixty times heavier than themselves by biting out their eyes and brain. This happened only when the fish were confined in containers with no room for escape. The same story has been told to me by fishermen on Lake Neusiedel, who could not possibly have heard Brehm's report. I once offered to my shrews a large edible frog. I never did it again, nor could I bear to see out to its end the cruel scene that ensued. One of the shrews encountered the frog in the basin and instantly gave chase, repeatedly seizing hold of the creature's legs; although it was kicked off again it did not cease in its attack and finally, the frog, in desperation, jumped out of the water and on to one of the tables, where several shrews raced to the pursuer's assistance and buried their teeth in the legs and hindquarters of the wretched frog. And now, horribly, they began to eat the frog alive, beginning just where each one of them happened to have hold of it; the poor frog croaked heartrendingly, as the jaws of the shrews munched audibly in chorus. I need hardly be blamed for bringing this experiment to an abrupt and agitated end and putting the lacerated frog out of its misery. I never offered the shrews large prey again but only such as would be killed at the first bite or two. Nature can be very cruel indeed; it is not out of pity that most of the larger predatory animals kill their prey quickly. The lion has to finish off a big antelope or a buffalo very quickly indeed in order not to get hurt itself, for a beast of prey which has to hunt daily cannot afford to receive even a harmless scratch in effecting a kill, such scratches would soon add up to such an extent as to put the killer out of action. The same reason has forced the python and other large snakes to evolve a quick and really humane method of killing the well-armed mammals that are their natural prey. But where there is no danger of the victim doing damage to the killer, the latter shows no pity whatsoever. The hedgehog which, by virtue of its armour, is quite immune to the bite of a snake, regularly proceeds to eat it, beginning at the tail or in the middle of its body, and in the same way the water-shrew treats its innocuous prey. But man should abstain from judging his innocently-cruel fellow creatures, for even if nature sometimes "shrieks against his creed," what pain does he himself not inflict upon the living creatures that he hunts for pleasure and not for food?

The mental qualities of the water-shrew cannot be rated very high. They were quite tame and fearless of me and never tried to bite when I took them in my hand, nor did they ever try to evade it, but, like little tame rodents, they tried to dig their way out if I held them for too long in the hollow of my closed fist. Even when I took them out of their container and put them on a table or on the floor, they were by no means thrown into a panic but were quite ready to take food out of my hand and even tried actively to creep into it if they felt a longing for cover. When, in such an unwonted environment, they were shown their nest-box, they plainly showed that they knew it by sight and instantly made for it, and even pursued it with upraised heads if I moved the box along above them, just out of their reach. All in all, I really may pride myself that I have tamed the shrew, or at least one member of that family.

In their accustomed surroundings, my shrews proved to be very strict creatures of habit. I have already mentioned the remarkable conservatism with which they persevered in their unpractical way of entering their nest-box by climbing on to its roof and then vaulting, with a half turn, in through the door. Something more must be said about the unchanging tenacity with which these animals cling to their habits once they have formed them. In the water-shrew, the path-habits, in particular, are of a really amazing immutability; I hardly know another instance to which the saying, "As the twig is bent, so the tree is inclined," applies so literally.

In a territory unknown to it, the water-shrew will never run fast except under pressure of extreme fear, and then it will run blindly along, bumping into objects and usually getting caught in a blind alley. But, unless the little animal is severely frightened, it moves, in strange surroundings, only step by step, whiskering right and left all the time and following a path that is anything but straight. Its course is determined by a hundred fortuitous factors when it walks that way for the first time. But, after a few repetitions, it is evident that the shrew recognizes the locality in which it finds itself and that it repeats, with the utmost exactitude, the movements which it performed the previous time. At the same time, it is notice-able that the animal moves along much faster whenever it is repeat-ing what it has already learned. When placed on a path which it has already traversed a few times, the shrew starts on its way slowly, carefully whiskering. Suddenly it finds known bearings, and now rushes forward a short distance, repeating exactly every step and turn which it executed on the last occasion. Then, when it comes to a spot where it ceases to know the way by heart, it is reduced to whiskering again and to feeling its way step by step. Soon, an-other burst of speed follows and the same thing is repeated, bursts of speed alternating with very slow progress. In the beginning of this process of learning their way, the shrews move along at an extremely slow average rate and the little bursts of speed are few and far between. But gradually the little laps of the course which have been "learned by heart" and which can be covered quickly begin to increase in length as well as in number until they fuse and the whole course can be completed in a fast, unbroken rush.

Often, when such a path-habit is almost completely formed, there still remains one particularly difficult place where the shrew always loses its bearings and has to resort to its senses of smell and touch, sniffing and whiskering vigorously to find out where the next reach of its path "joins on." Once the shrew is well settled in its path-habits it is as strictly bound to them as a railway engine to its tracks and as unable to deviate from them by even a few centimeters. If it diverges from its path by so much as an inch, it is forced to stop abruptly, and laboriously regain its bearings. The same behaviour can be caused experimentally by changing some small detail in the customary path of the animal. Any major alteration in the habitual path threw the shrews into complete confusion. One of their paths ran along the wall adjoining the wooden table opposite to that on which the nest box was situated. This table was weighted with two stones lying close to the panes of the tank, and the shrews, running along the wall, were accustomed to jump on and off the stones which lay right in their path. If I moved the stones out of the runway, placing both together in the middle of the table, the shrews would jump right up into the air in the place where the stone should have been; they came down with a jarring bump, were obvi-ously disconcerted and started whiskering cautiously right and left, just as they behaved in an unknown environment. And then they did a most interesting thing: they went back the way they had come, carefully feeling their way until they had again got their bearings. Then, facing round again, they tried a second time with a rush and jumped and crashed down exactly as they had done a few seconds before. Only then did they seem to realize that the first fall had not been their own fault but was due to a change in the wonted pathway, and now they proceeded to explore the alteration, cautiously sniffing and be-whiskering the place where the stone ought to have been. This method of going back to the start, and trying again always reminded me of a small boy who, in reciting a poem, gets stuck and begins again at an earlier verse.

In rats, as in many small mammals, the process of forming a path-habit, for instance in learning a maze, is very similar to that just described; but a rat is far more adaptable in its behaviour and would not dream of trying to jump over a stone which was not there. The preponderance of motor habit over present perception is a most remarkable peculiarity of the water-shrew. One might say that the animal actually disbelieves its senses if they report a change of environment which necessitates a sudden alteration in its motor habits. In a new environment a water-shrew would be perfectly able to see a stone of that size and consequently to avoid it or to run over it in a manner well adapted to the spatial conditions; but once a habit is formed and has become ingrained, it supersedes all better knowledge. I know of no animal that is a slave to its habits in so literal a sense as the water-shrew. For this animal the geometric axiom that a straight line is the shortest distance between two points simply does not hold good. To them, the shortest line is always the accustomed path and, to a certain extent, they are justified in adhering to this principle: they run with amazing speed along their pathways and arrive at their destination much sooner than they would if, by whiskering and nosing, they tried to go straight. They will keep to the wonted path, even though it winds in such a way that it crosses and recrosses itself. A rat or mouse would be quick to discover that it was making an unnecessary detour, but the water-shrew is no more able to do so than is a toy train to turn off at right angles at a level crossing. In order to change its route, the water-shrew must change its whole path-habit, and this cannot be done at a moment's notice but gradually, over a long period of time. An unnecessary, loop-shaped detour takes weeks and weeks to become a little shorter, and after months it is not even approximately straight. The biological advantage of such a path-habit is obvious: it compensates the shrew for being nearly blind and enables it to run exceedingly fast without wasting a minute on orientation. On the other hand it may, under unusual circumstances, lead the shrew to destruction. It has been reported, quite plausibly, that water-shrews have broken their necks by jumping into a pond which had been recently drained. In spite of the possibility of such mishaps, it would be short-sighted if one were simply to stigmatize the water-shrew as stupid because it solves the spatial problems of its daily life in quite a different way from man. On the contrary, if one thinks a little more deeply, it is very wonderful that the same result, namely a perfect orientation in space, can be brought about in two so widely divergent ways: by true observation, as we achieve it, or, as the water-shrew does, by learning by heart every possible spatial contingency that may arise in a given territory.

Among themselves, my water-shrews were surprisingly good-natured. Although, in their play, they would often chase each other, twittering with a great show of excitement, I never saw a serious fight between them until an unfortunate accident occurred: one morning, I forgot to reopen the little door of the nest-box after cleaning out their tank. When at last I remembered, three hours had elapsed—a very long time for the swift metabolism of such small insectivores. Upon the opening of the door, all the shrews rushed out and made a dash for the food tray. In their haste to get out, not only did they soil themselves all over but they apparently discharged, in their excitement, some sort of glandular secretion, for a strong, musk-like odour accompanied their exit from the box. Since they appeared to have incurred no damage by their three hours' fasting, I turned away from the box to occupy myself with other things. However, on nearing the container soon afterwards, I heard an unusually loud, sharp twittering and, on my hurried approach, found my eight shrews locked in deadly battle. Two were even then dying and, though I consigned them at once to separate cages, two more died in the course of the day. The real cause of this sudden and terrible battle is hard to ascertain but I cannot help suspecting that the shrews, owing to the sudden change in the usual odour, had failed to recognize each other and had fallen upon each other as they would have done upon strangers. The four survivors quietened down after a certain time and I was able to reunite them in the original container without fear of further mishap.

I kept those four remaining shrews in good health for nearly seven months and would probably have had them much longer if the assistant whom I had engaged to feed them had not forgotten to do so. I had been obliged to go to Vienna and, on my return in the late afternoon, was met by that usually reliable fellow who turned pale when he saw me, thereupon remembering that he had forgotten to feed the shrews. All four of them were alive but very weak; they ate greedily when we fed them but died none the less within a few hours. In other words, they showed exactly the same symptoms as the shrews which I had formerly tried to keep; this confirmed my opinion that the latter were already dying of hunger when they came into my possession.

To any advanced animal keeper who is able to set up a large tank, preferably with running water, and who can obtain a sufficient supply of small fish, tadpoles and the like, I can recommend the water-shrew as one of the most gratifying, charming and interesting objects of care. Of course it is a somewhat exacting charge. It will eat raw chopped heart (the customary substitute for small live prey) only in the absence of something better and it cannot be fed exclusively on this diet for long periods. Moreover, really clean water is indispensable. But if these clear-cut requirements be fulfilled, the water-shrew will not merely remain alive but will really thrive, nor do I exclude the possibility that it might even breed in captivity.

[5]

The Nature of Love [1]

HARRY F. HARLOW

Love is a wondrous state, deep, tender, and rewarding. Because of its intimate and personal nature it is regarded by some as an improper topic for experimental research. But, whatever our personal feelings may be, our assigned mission as psychologists is to analyze all facets of human and animal behavior into their component variables. So far as love or affection is concerned, psychologists have failed in this mission. The little we know about love does not transcend simple observation, and the little we write about it has been written better by poets and novelists. But of greater concern is the fact that psychologists tend to give progressively less attention to a motive which pervades our entire lives. Psychologists, at least psychologists who write textbooks, not only show no interest in the origin and development of love or affection, but they seem to be unaware of its very existence.

The apparent repression of love by modern psychologists stands in sharp contrast with the attitude taken by many famous and normal people. The word *love* has the highest reference frequency of any word cited in Bartlett's book of *Familiar Quotations*. It would appear that this emotion has long had a vast interest and fascination for human beings, regardless of the attitude taken by psychologists; but the quotations cited, even by famous and normal people, have a mundane redundancy. These authors and authorities have stolen love from the child and infant and made it the exclusive property of the adolescent and adult.

Thoughtful men, and probably all women, have speculated on

[1] Address of the President at the sixty-sixth Annual Convention of the American Psychological Association, Washington, D.C., August 31, 1958. The researches reported in this paper were supported by funds supplied by Grant No. M–722, National Institutes of Health, by a grant from the Ford Foundation, and by funds received from the Graduate School of the University of Wisconsin.

SOURCE: Harry F. Harlow, "The Nature of Love," *American Psychologist*, 1958, 13, pp. 673–685. Reprinted by permission of the American Psychological Association and Harry F. Harlow.

the nature of love. From the developmental point of view, the general plan is quite clear: The initial love responses of the human being are those made by the infant to the mother or some mother surrogate. From this intimate attachment of the child to the mother, multiple learned and generalized affectional responses are formed.

Unfortunately, beyond these simple facts we know little about the fundamental variables underlying the formation of affectional responses and little about the mechanisms through which the love of the infant for the mother develops into the multifaceted response patterns characterizing love or affection in the adult. Because of the dearth of experimentation, theories about the fundamental nature of affection have evolved at the level of observation, intuition, and discerning guesswork, whether these have been proposed by psychologists, sociologists, anthropologists, physicians, or psychoanalysts.

The position commonly held by psychologists and sociologists is quite clear: The basic motives are, for the most part, the primary drives—particularly hunger, thirst, elimination, pain, and sex—and all other motives, including love or affection, are derived or secondary drives. The mother is associated with the reduction of the primary drives—particularly hunger, thirst, and pain—and through learning, affection or love is derived.

It is entirely reasonable to believe that the mother through association with food may become a secondary-reinforcing agent, but this is an inadequate mechanism to account for the persistence of the infant-maternal ties. There is a spate of researches on the formation of secondary reinforcers to hunger and thirst reduction. There can be no question that almost any external stimulus can become a secondary reinforcer if properly associated with tissue-need reduction, but the fact remains that this redundant literature demonstrates unequivocally that such derived drives suffer relatively rapid experimental extinction. Contrariwise, human affection does not extinguish when the mother ceases to have intimate association with the drives in question. Instead, the affectional ties to the mother show a lifelong, unrelenting persistence and, even more surprising, widely expanding generality.

Oddly enough, one of the few psychologists who took a position counter to modern psychological dogma was John B. Watson, who believed that love was an innate emotion elicited by cutaneous stimulation of the erogenous zones. But experimental psychologists, with their peculiar propensity to discover facts that are not true, brushed this theory aside by demonstrating that the human neonate had no differentiable emotions, and they established a fundamental psychological law that prophets are without honor in their own profession.

The psychoanalysts have concerned themselves with the problem of the nature of the development of love in the neonate and infant, using ill and aging human beings as subjects. They have discovered the overwhelming importance of the breast and related this to the oral erotic tendencies developed at an age preceding their subjects' memories. Their theories range from a belief that the infant has an innate need to achieve and suckle at the breast to beliefs not unlike commonly accepted psychological theories. There are exceptions, as seen in the recent writings of John Bowlby, who attributes importance not only to food and thirst satisfaction, but also to "primary object-clinging," a need for intimate physical contact, which is initially associated with the mother.

As far as I know, there exists no direct experimental analysis of the relative importance of the stimulus variables determining the affectional or love responses in the neonatal and infant primate. Unfortunately, the human neonate is a limited experimental subject for such researches because of his inadequate motor capabilities. By the time the human infant's motor responses can be precisely measured, the antecedent determining conditions cannot be defined, having been lost in a jumble and jungle of confounded variables.

Many of these difficulties can be resolved by the use of the neonatal and infant macaque monkey as the subject for the analysis of basic affectional variables. It is possible to make precise measurements in this primate beginning at two to ten days of age, depending upon the maturational status of the individual animal at birth. The macaque infant differs from the human infant in that the monkey is more mature at birth and grows more rapidly; but the basic responses relating to affection, including nursing, contact, clinging, and even visual and auditory exploration, exhibit no fundamental differences in the two species. Even the development of perception, fear, frustration, and learning capability follows very similar sequences in rhesus monkeys and human children.

Three years' experimentation before we started our studies on affection gave us experience with the neonatal monkey. We had separated more than 60 of these animals from their mothers 6 to 12 hours after birth and suckled them on tiny bottles. The infant mortality was only a small fraction of what would have obtained had we let the monkey mothers raise their infants. Our bottle-fed babies were healthier and heavier than monkey-mother-reared infants. We know that we are better monkey mothers than are real monkey mothers thanks to synthetic diets, vitamins, iron extracts, penicillin, chloromycetin, 5 percent glucose, and constant, tender, loving care.

During the course of these studies we noticed that the laboratory-raised babies showed strong attachment to the cloth pads (folded gauze diapers) which were used to cover the hardware-cloth floors of their cages. The infants clung to these pads and engaged in violent temper tantrums when the pads were removed and replaced for sanitary reasons. Such contact-need or responsiveness had been reported previously by Gertrude van Wagenen for the monkey and by Thomas McCulloch and George Haslerud for the chimpanzee and is reminiscent of the devotion often exhibited by human infants to their pillows, blankets, and soft, cuddly stuffed toys. . . . The baby, human or monkey, if it is to survive, must clutch at more than a straw.

We had also discovered during some allied observational studies that a baby monkey raised on a bare wire-mesh cage floor survives with difficulty, if at all, during the first five days of life. If a wire-mesh cone is introduced, the baby does better; and, if the cone is covered with terry cloth, husky, healthy, happy babies evolve. It takes more than a baby and a box to make a normal monkey. We were impressed by the possibility that, above and beyond the bubbling fountain of breast or bottle, contact comfort might be a very important variable in the development of the infant's affection for the mother.

At this point we decided to study the development of affectional responses of neonatal and infant monkeys to an artificial, inanimate mother, and so we built a surrogate mother which we hoped and believed would be a good surrogate mother. In devising this surrogate mother we were dependent neither upon the capriciousness of evolutionary processes nor upon mutations produced by chance radioactive fallout. Instead, we designed the mother surrogate in terms of modern human-engineering principles. We produced a perfectly proportioned, streamlined body stripped of unnecessary bulges and appendices. Redundancy in the surrogate mother's system was avoided by reducing the number of breasts from two to one and placing this unibreast in an upper-thoracic, sagittal position, thus maximizing the natural and known perceptual-motor capabilities of the infant operator. The surrogate was made from a block of wood, covered with sponge rubber, and sheathed in tan cotton terry cloth. A light bulb behind her radiated heat. The result was a mother, soft, warm, and tender, a mother with infinite patience, a mother available twenty-four hours a day, a mother that never scolded her infant and never struck or bit her baby in anger. Furthermore, we designed a mother-machine with maximal maintenance efficiency since failure of any system or function could be resolved by the simple substitution of black boxes and new component parts. It is our opinion that we engineered a very superior monkey mother, although this position is not held universally by the monkey fathers.

Before beginning our initial experiment we also designed and constructed a second mother surrogate, a surrogate in which we deliberately built less than the maximal capability for contact comfort. This surrogate mother is . . . made of wire-mesh, a substance entirely adequate to provide postural support and nursing capability, and she is warmed by radiant heat. Her body differs in no essential way from that of the cloth mother surrogate other than in the quality of the contact comfort which she can supply.

In our initial experiment, the dual mother-surrogate condition, a cloth mother and a wire mother were placed in different cubicles attached to the infant's living cage. . . . For four newborn monkeys the cloth mother lactated and the wire mother did not; and, for the other four, this condition was reversed. In either condition the infant received all its milk through the mother surrogate as soon as it was able to maintain itself in this way, a capability achieved within two or three days except in the case of very immature infants. Supplementary feedings were given until the milk intake from the mother surrogate was adequate. Thus, the experiment was designed as a test of the relative importance of the variables of contact comfort and nursing comfort. During the first 14 days of life the monkey's cage floor was covered with a heating pad wrapped in a folded gauze diaper, and thereafter the cage floor was bare. The infants were always free to leave the heating pad or cage floor to contact either mother, and the time spent on the surrogate mothers was automatically recorded. Figure 1 shows the total time spent on the

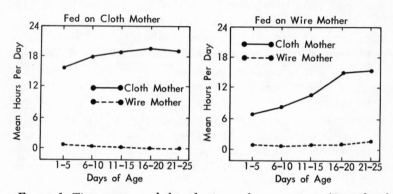

FIGURE 1. Time spent on cloth and wire mother surrogates. (Reproduced from Figure 5 from Harry F. Harlow, "The Nature of Love," *American Psychologist*, 1958, 13. Reprinted by permission of the American Psychological Association and Harry F. Harlow.)

cloth and wire mothers under the two conditions of feeding. These data make it obvious that contact comfort is a variable of overwhelming importance in the development of affectional responses, whereas lactation is a variable of negligible importance. With age and opportunity to learn, subjects with the lactating wire mother showed decreasing responsiveness to her and increasing responsiveness to the nonlactating cloth mother, a finding completely contrary to any interpretation of derived drive in which the mother-form becomes conditioned to hunger-thirst reduction. The persistence of these differential responses throughout 165 consecutive days of testing is evident in Figure 2.

One control group of neonatal monkeys was raised on a single wire mother, and a second control group was raised on a single cloth mother. There were no differences between these two groups in amount of milk ingested or in weight gain. The only difference between the groups lay in the composition of the feces, the softer stools of the wire-mother infants suggesting psychosomatic involvement. The wire mother is biologically adequate but psychologically inept.

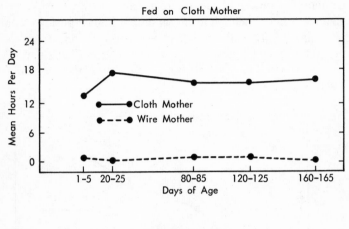

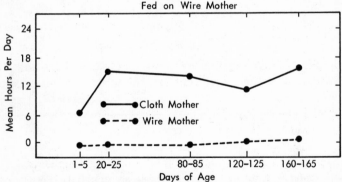

FIGURE 2. Long-term contact time on cloth and wire mother surrogates. (Reproduced from Figure 6 from Harry F. Harlow, "The Nature of Love," *American Psychologist*, 1958, **13**. Reprinted by permission of the American Psychological Association and Harry F. Harlow.)

We were not surprised to discover that contact comfort was an important basic affectional or love variable, but we did not expect it to overshadow so completely the variable of nursing; indeed, the disparity is so great as to suggest that the primary function of nursing as an affectional variable is that of insuring frequent and intimate body contact of the infant with the mother. Certainly, man cannot live by milk alone. Love is an emotion that does not need to be bottle- or spoon-fed, and we may be sure that there is nothing to be gained by giving lip service to love.

A charming lady once heard me describe these experiments; and, when I subsequently talked to her, her face brightened with sudden insight: "Now I know what's wrong with me," she said, "I'm just a wire mother." Perhaps she was lucky. She might have been a wire wife.

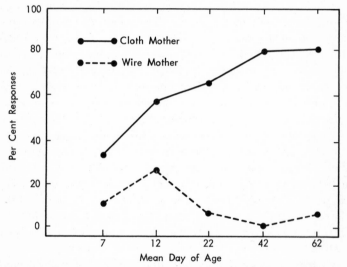

FIGURE 3. Differential responsiveness in fear tests. (Reproduced from Figure 15 from Harry F. Harlow, "The Nature of Love," *American Psychologist*, 1958, **13**. Reprinted by permission of the American Psychological Association and Harry F. Harlow.)

One function of the real mother, human or subhuman, and presumably of a mother surrogate, is to provide a haven of safety for the infant in times of fear and danger. The frightened or ailing child clings to its mother, not its father; and this selective responsiveness in times of distress, disturbance, or danger may be used as a measure of the strength of affectional bonds. We have tested this kind of differential responsiveness by presenting to the infants in their cages, in the presence of the two mothers, various fear-producing stimuli . . . and the data on differential responsiveness are presented in Figure 3. It is apparent that the cloth mother is highly preferred over the wire one, and this differential selectivity is enhanced by age and experience. In this situation, the variable of nursing appears to be of absolutely no importance: the infant consistently seeks the soft mother surrogate regardless of nursing condition.

Similarly, the mother or mother surrogate provides its young with a source of security, and this role or function is seen with special clarity when mother and child are in a strange situation. At the present time we have completed tests for this relationship on four of our eight baby monkeys assigned to the dual mother-surrogate condition by introducing them for three minutes into the strange environment of a room measuring six feet by six feet by six feet (also called the "open-field test") and containing multiple stimuli known to elicit curiosity-manipulatory responses in baby monkeys. The subjects were placed in this situation twice a week for eight weeks with no mother surrogate present during alternate sessions and the cloth mother present during the others. A cloth diaper was always available as one of the stimuli throughout all sessions. After one or two adaptation sessions, the infants always rushed to the mother surrogate when she was present and clutched her, rubbed their bodies against her, and frequently manipulated her body and face. After a few additional sessions, the infants began to use the mother surrogate as a source of security, a base of operations. . . . They would explore and manipulate a stimulus and then return to the mother before adventuring again into the strange new world. The behavior of these infants was quite different when the mother was absent from the room. Frequently they would freeze in a crouched position. . . . Emotionally indices such as vocalization, crouching, rocking, and sucking increased sharply, as shown in Figure 4. Total emotionality score was cut in half when the mother was present. In the absence of the mother some of the experimental monkeys would rush to the center of the room where the mother was customarily placed and then run rapidly from object to object, screaming and crying all the while. Continuous, frantic clutching of their bodies was very common, even when not in the crouching position. These monkeys frequently contacted and clutched the cloth diaper, but this action never pacified them. The same behavior occurred in the presence of the wire mother. No difference between the cloth-mother-fed and wire-mother-fed infants was demonstrated under either condition. Four control infants never raised with a mother surrogate showed the same emotionality scores when the mother was absent as the experimental infants showed in the absence of the mother, but the controls' scores were slightly larger in the presence of the mother surrogate than in her absence.

Some years ago Robert Butler demonstrated that mature monkeys

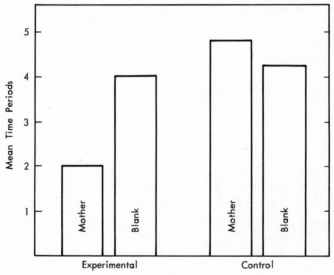

Figure 4. Emotionality index with and without the presence of the cloth mother. (Reproduced from Figure 20 from Harry F. Harlow, "The Nature of Love," *American Psychologist,* 1958, **13.** Reprinted by permission of the American Psychological Association and Harry F. Harlow.)

enclosed in a dimly lighted box would open and reopen a door hour after hour for no other reward than that of looking outside the box. We now have data indicating that neonatal monkeys show this same compulsive visual curiosity on their first test day in an adaptation of the Butler apparatus which we call the "love machine," an apparatus designed to measure love. Usually these tests are begun when the monkey is 10 days of age, but this same persistent visual exploration has been obtained in a three-day-old monkey during the first half-hour of testing. Butler also demonstrated that rhesus monkeys show selectivity in rate and frequency of door-opening to stimuli of differential attractiveness in the visual field outside the box. We have utilized this principle of response selectivity by the monkey to measure strength of affectional responsiveness in our infants in the baby version of the Butler box. The test sequence involves four repetitions of a test battery in which four stimuli—cloth mother, wire mother, infant monkey, and empty box—are presented for a 30-minute period on successive days. The first four subjects in the

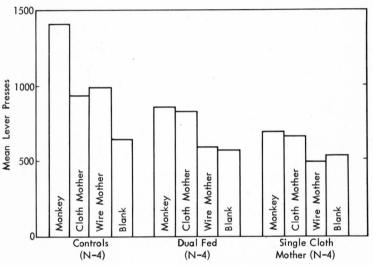

FIGURE 5. Differential responses to visual exploration. (Reproduced from Figure 22 from Harry F. Harlow, "The Nature of Love," *American Psychologist,* 1958, **13.** Reprinted by permission of the American Psychological Association and Harry F. Harlow.)

dual mother-surrogate group were given a single test sequence at 40 to 50 days of age, depending upon the availability of the apparatus, and only their data are presented. The second set of four subjects is being given repetitive tests to obtain information relating to the development of visual exploration. . . . The data obtained from the first four infants raised with the two mother surrogates are presented in the middle graph of Figure 5 and show approximately equal responding to the cloth mother and another infant monkey, and no greater responsiveness to the wire mother than to an empty box. Again, the results are independent of the kind of mother that lactated, cloth or wire. The same results are found for a control group raised, but not fed, on a single cloth mother; these data appear in the graph on the right. Contrariwise, the graph on the left shows no differential responsiveness to cloth and wire mothers by a second control group, which was not raised on any mother surrogate. We can be certain that not all love is blind.

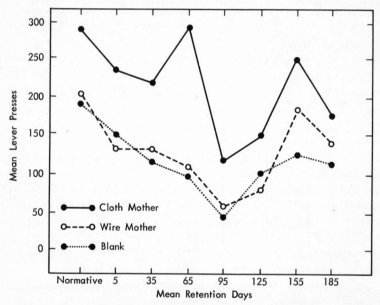

Figure 6. Retention of differential visual-exploration responses. (Reproduced from Figure 23 from Harry F. Harlow, "The Nature of Love," *American Psychologist*, 1958, **13**. Reprinted by permission of the American Psychological Association and Harry F. Harlow.)

The first four infant monkeys in the dual mother-surrogate group were separated from their mothers between 165 and 170 days of age and tested for retention during the following 9 days and then at 30-day intervals for six successive months. Affectional retention as measured by the modified Butler box is given in Figure 6. In keeping with the data obtained on adult monkeys by Butler, we find a high rate of responding to any stimulus, even the empty box. But throughout the entire 185-day retention period there is a consistent and significant difference in response frequency to the cloth mother contrasted with either the wire mother or the empty box, and no consistent difference between wire mother and empty box.

Affectional retention was also tested in the open field during the first 9 days after separation and then at 30-day intervals, and each test condition was run twice at each retention interval. The infant's behavior differed from that observed during the period preceding separation. When the cloth mother was present in the post-separation period, the babies rushed to her, climbed up, clung tightly to her, and rubbed their heads and faces against her body. After this initial embrace and reunion, they played on the mother, including biting and tearing at her cloth cover; but they rarely made any attempt to leave her during the test period, nor did they manipulate or play with the objects in the room, in contrast with their behavior before maternal separation. The only exception was the occasional monkey that left the mother surrogate momentarily, grasped the folded piece of paper (one of the standard stimuli in the field), and brought it quickly back to the mother. It appeared that deprivation had enhanced the tie to the mother and rendered the contact-comfort need so prepotent that need for the mother overwhelmed the exploratory motives during the brief, three-minute test sessions. No change in these behaviors was observed throughout the 185-day period. When the mother was absent from the open field, the behavior of the infants was similar in the initial retention test to that during the preseparation tests; but they tended to show gradual adaptation to the open-field situation with repeated testing and, consequently, a reduction in their emotionality scores.

In the last five retention test periods, an additional test was introduced in which the surrogate mother was placed in the center of the room and covered with a clear Plexiglas box. The monkeys were initially disturbed and frustrated when their explorations and manipulations of the box failed to provide contact with the mother. However, all animals adapted to the situation rather rapidly. Soon they used the box as a place of orientation for exploratory and play behavior, made frequent contacts with the objects in the field, and very often brought these objects to the Plexiglas box. The emotionality index was slightly higher than in the condition of the available cloth mothers, but it in no way approached the emotionality level displayed when the cloth mother was absent. Obviously, the infant monkeys gained emotional security by the presence of the mother even though contact was denied.

Affectional retention has also been measured by tests in which the monkey must unfasten a three-device mechanical puzzle to obtain entrance into a compartment containing the mother surrogate. All the trials are initiated by allowing the infant to go through an unlocked door, and in half the trials it finds the mother present and in half, an empty compartment. The door is then locked and

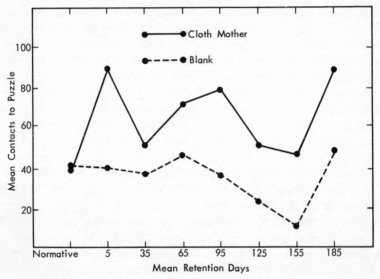

FIGURE 7. Retention of puzzle manipulation responsiveness. (Reproduced from Figure 24 from Harry F. Harlow, "The Nature of Love," *American Psychologist,* 1958, **13.** Reprinted by permission of the American Psychological Association and Harry F. Harlow.)

a ten-minute test conducted. In tests given prior to separation from the surrogate mothers, some of the infants had solved this puzzle and others had failed. The data of Figure 7 show that on the last test before separation there were no differences in total manipulation under mother-present and mother-absent conditions, but striking differences exist between the two conditions throughout the post-separation test periods. Again, there is no interaction with conditions of feeding.

The over-all picture obtained from surveying the retention data is unequivocal. There is little, if any, waning of responsiveness to the mother throughout this five-month period as indicated by any measure. It becomes perfectly obvious that this affectional bond is highly resistant to forgetting and that it can be retained for very long periods of time by relatively infrequent contact reinforcement. During the next year, retention tests will be conducted at 90-day intervals, and further plans are dependent upon the results obtained. It would appear that affectional responses may show as much resistance to extinction as has been previously demonstrated for learned fears and learned pain, and such data would be in keeping with those of common human observation.

The infant's responses to the mother surrogate in the fear tests, the open-field situation, and the baby Butler box and the responses on the retention tests cannot be described adequately with words. For supplementary information we turn to the motion picture record. (At this point a 20-minute film was presented illustrating and supplementing the behaviors described thus far in the address.)

We have already described the group of four control infants that had never lived in the presence of any mother surrogate and had demonstrated no sign of affection or security in the presence of the cloth mothers introduced in test sessions. When these infants reached the age of 250 days, cubicles containing both a cloth mother and a wire mother were attached to their cages. There was no lactation in these mothers, for the monkeys were on a solid-food diet. The initial reaction of the monkeys to the alterations was one of extreme disturbance. All the infants screamed violently and made repeated attempts to escape the cage whenever the door was opened. They kept a maximum distance from the mother surrogates and exhibited a considerable amount of rocking and crouching behavior, indicative of emotionality. Our first thought was that the critical period for the development of maternally directed affection had passed and that these macaque children were doomed to live as affectional orphans. Fortunately, these behaviors continued for only 12 to 48 hours and then gradually ebbed, changing from indifference to active contact on, and exploration of, the surrogates. The home-cage behavior of these control monkeys slowly became similar to that of the animals raised with the mother surrogates from birth. Their manipulation and play on the cloth mother became progressively more vigorous to the point of actual mutilation, particularly during the morning after the cloth mother had been given her daily change of terry covering. The control subjects were now actively running to the cloth mother when frightened and had to be coaxed from her to be taken from the cage for formal testing.

Objective evidence of these changing behaviors is given in Figure 8, which plots the amount of time these infants spent on the mother

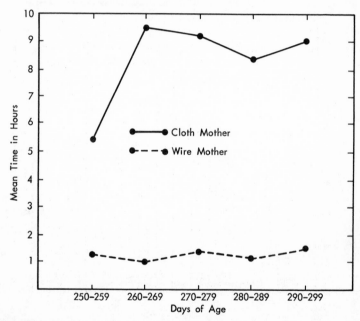

FIGURE 8. Differential time spent on cloth and wire mother surrogates by monkeys started at 250 days of age. (Reproduced from Figure 25 from Harry F. Harlow, "The Nature of Love," *American Psychologist*, 1958, **13**. Reprinted by permission of the American Psychological Association and Harry F. Harlow.)

surrogates. Within 10 days mean contact time is approximately nine hours, and this measure remains relatively constant throughout the next 30 days. Consistent with the results on the subjects reared from birth with dual mothers, these late-adopted infants spent less than one and one-half hours per day in contact with the wire mothers, and this activity level was relatively constant throughout the test sessions. Although the maximum time that the control monkeys spent on the cloth mother was only about half that spent by the original dual mother-surrogate group, we cannot be sure that this discrepancy is a function of differential early experience. The control monkeys were about three months older when the mothers were attached to their cages than the experimental animals had been when their mothers were removed and the retention tests begun. Thus, we do not know what the amount of contact would be for a 250-day-old

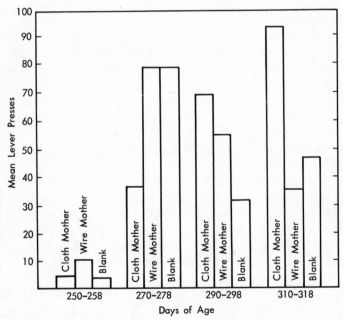

FIGURE 9. Differential visual exploration of monkeys started at 250 days of age. (Reproduced from Figure 26 from Harry F. Harlow, "The Nature of Love," *American Psychologist,* 1958, **13.** Reprinted by permission of the American Psychological Association and Harry F. Harlow.)

animal raised from birth with surrogate mothers. Nevertheless, the magnitude of the differences and the fact that the contact-time curves for the mothered-from-birth infants had remained constant for almost 150 days suggest that early experience with the mother is a variable of measurable importance.

The control group has also been tested for differential visual exploration after the introduction of the cloth and wire mothers; these behaviors are plotted in Figure 9. By the second test session a high level of exploratory behavior had developed, and the responsiveness to the wire mother and the empty box is significantly greater than that to the cloth mother. This is probably not an artifact since there is every reason to believe that the face of the cloth mother is a fear stimulus to most monkeys that have not had extensive experience with this object during the first 40 to 60 days of life. Within the third test session a sharp change in trend occurs, and the cloth mother is then more frequently viewed than the wire mother or the blank box; this trend continues during the fourth session, producing a significant preference for the cloth mother.

Before the introduction of the mother surrogate into the home-cage situation, only one of the four control monkeys had ever contacted the cloth mother in the open-field tests. In general, the surrogate mother not only gave the infants no security, but instead appeared to serve as a fear stimulus. The emotionality scores of these control subjects were slightly higher during the mother-present test sessions than during the mother-absent test sessions. These behaviors were changed radically by the fourth post-introduction test approximately 60 days later. In the absence of the cloth mothers the emotionality index in this fourth test remains near the earlier level, but the score is reduced by half when the mother is present, a result strikingly similar to that found for infants raised with the dual mother-surrogates from birth. The control infants now show increasing object exploration and play behavior, and they begin to use the mother as a base of operations, as did the infants raised from birth with the mother surrogates. However, there are still definite differences in the behavior of the two groups. The control infants do not rush directly to the mother and clutch her violently; but instead they go toward, and orient around, her, usually after an initial period during which they frequently show disturbed behavior, exploratory behavior, or both.

That the control monkeys develop affection or love for the cloth mother when she is introduced into the cage at 250 days of age cannot be questioned. There is every reason to believe, however, that this interval of delay depresses the intensity of the affectional response below that of the infant monkeys that were surrogate-mothered from birth onward. In interpreting these data it is well to remember that the control monkeys had had continuous opportunity to observe and hear other monkeys housed in adjacent cages and that they had had limited opportunity to view and contact surrogate mothers in the test situations, even though they did not exploit the opportunities.

During the last two years we have observed the behavior of two infants raised by their own mothers. Love for the real mother and love for the surrogate mother appear to be very similar. The baby macaque spends many hours a day clinging to its real mother. If away from the mother when frightened, it rushes to her and in her presence shows comfort and composure. As far as we can observe, the infant monkey's affection for the real mother is strong, but no stronger than that of the experimental monkey for the surrogate cloth mother, and the security that the infant gains from the presence of the real mother is no greater than the security it gains from a cloth surrogate. Next year we hope to put this problem to final, definitive, experimental test. But, whether the mother is real or a cloth surrogate, there does develop a deep and abiding bond between mother and child. In one case it may be the call of the wild and in the other the McCall of civilization, but in both cases there is "togetherness."

In spite of the importance of contact comfort, there is reason to believe that other variables of measurable importance will be discovered. Postural support may be such a variable, and it has been suggested that, when we build arms into the mother surrogate, 10 is the minimal number required to provide adequate child care. Rocking motion may be such a variable, and we are comparing rocking and stationary mother surrogates and inclined planes. The differential responsiveness to cloth mother and cloth-covered inclined plane suggests that clinging as well as contact is an effectional variable of importance. Sounds, particularly natural, maternal sounds, may operate as either unlearned or learned affectional variables. Visual responsiveness may be such a variable, and it is possible that some semblance of visual imprinting may develop in the neonatal monkey.

There are indications that this becomes a variable of importance during the course of infancy through some maturational process.

John Bowlby has suggested that there is an affectional variable which he calls "primary object following," characterized by visual and oral search of the mother's face. Our surrogate-mother-raised baby monkeys are at first inattentive to her face, as are human neonates to human mother faces. But by 30 days of age ever-increasing responsiveness to the mother's face appears—whether through learning, maturation, or both—and we have reason to believe that the face becomes an object of special attention.

Our first surrogate-mother-raised baby had a mother whose head was just a ball of wood since the baby was a month early and we had not had time to design a more esthetic head and face. This baby had contact with the blank-faced mother for 180 days and was then placed with two cloth mothers, one motionless and one rocking, both being endowed with painted, ornamented faces. To our surprise the animal would compulsively rotate both faces 180 degrees so that it viewed only a round, smooth face and never the painted, ornamented face. Furthermore, it would do this as long as the patience of the experimenter in reorienting the faces persisted. The monkey showed no sign of fear or anxiety, but it showed unlimited persistence. Subsequently it improved its technique compulsively removing the heads and rolling them into its cage as fast as they were returned. We are intrigued by this observation, and we plan to examine systematically the role of the mother face in the development of infant-monkey affections. Indeed, these observations suggest the need for a series of ethological-type researches on the two-faced female.

Although we have made no attempts thus far to study the generalization of infant-macaque affection or love, the techniques which we have developed offer promise in this uncharted field. Beyond this, there are few if any technical difficulties in studying the affection of the actual, living mother for the child, and the techniques developed can be utilized and expanded for the analysis and developmental study of father-infant and infant-infant affection.

Since we can measure neonatal and infant affectional responses to mother surrogates, and since we know they are strong and persisting, we are in a position to assess the effects of feeding and contactual schedules; consistency and inconsistency in the mother surrogates; and early, intermediate, and late maternal deprivation. Again, we have here a family of problems of fundamental interest and theoretical importance.

If the researches completed and proposed make a contribution, I shall be grateful; but I have also given full thought to possible practical applications. The socio-economic demands of the present and the threatened socioeconomic demands of the future have led the American woman to displace, or threaten to displace, the American man in science and industry. If this process continues, the problem of proper child-rearing practices faces us with startling clarity. It is cheering in view of this trend to realize that the American male is physically endowed with all the really essential equipment to compete with the American female on equal terms in one essential activity: the rearing of infants. We now know that women in the working classes are not needed in the home because of their primary mammalian capabilities; and it is possible that in the foreseeable future neonatal nursing will not be regarded as a necessity, but as a luxury—to use Veblen's term—a form of conspicuous consumption limited perhaps to the upper classes. But whatever course history may take, it is comforting to know that we are now in contact with the nature of love.

Bibliography

Alpers, A. *Dolphins: the myth and the mammal.* Cambridge, Mass.: Riverside, 1960.

Asimov, I. *The wellsprings of life.* New York: New American Library, 1962.

Bensberg, G. J. (Ed.) *Teaching the mentally retarded.* Atlanta, Ga.: Southern Regional Education Board, 1965.

Bitterman, M. E. Toward a comparative psychology of learning. *Amer. Psychol.*, 1960, **15**, 704–712.

Bitterman, M. E. The evolution of intelligence. *Sci. Amer.*, January 1965, **212** (1), 92–100.

Breland, K., and Breland, M. A field of applied animal psychology. *Amer. Psychol.*, 1951, **6** (6), 202–204.

Breland, K., and Breland, M. The misbehavior of organisms. *Amer. Psychol.*, 1961, **16**, 681–684.

Boyden, A., and Gemeroy, D. The relative position of the Cetacea among the orders of Mammalia as indicated by precipitin tests. *Zoologica*, 1950, **35** (2), 145–151.

Coon, C. S. *The origin of races.* New York: Knopf, 1962.

Darwin, C. *Origin of species.* 1859. New York: New American Library, 1960 (ed.).

Dembeck, H. *Animals and men.* New York: Natural History, 1965.

Descartes, R. On method. In Adler, M. (Ed.), *Great books*, **31**. Chicago: Encycl. Brit., 1952.

Dilger, W. C. The behavior of lovebirds. *Sci. Amer.*, January 1962, **206** (1), 89–98.

Ferster, C. B. Arithmetic behavior in chimpanzees. *Sci. Amer.*, 1964, **210** (5), 98–106.

Grossman, K. Behavioral differences between rabbits and cats. Unpublished doctoral dissertation, Univer. of Arkansas, 1965.

Guhl, A. M. Reflections by an animal behaviorist. *Trans. Kans. Acad. Sci.*, 1963, **66** (2), 171–185.

Hafez, E. S. E. (Ed.) *The behavior of domestic animals.* Baltimore: Williams and Wilkins, 1962.

Hayes, Cathy. *The ape in our house.* New York: Harper, 1951.

Hill, R. N. *Window in the sea.* New York: Holt, Rinehart, 1956.

Kellogg, W. N.   *Porpoises and sonar.* Chicago: Univer. of Chicago, 1961.

Kuo, Z. Y.   Ontogeny of embryonic behavior in aves, Part IV. *J. comp. Psychol.*, 1932, **14**, 109–122.

Lane, H.   Operant control of vocalizing in the chicken. *J. exp. anal. Behav.*, 1961, **4**, 171–177.

Layne, J. N.   Observations on marine mammals in Florida waters. *Bull. Fla. State Museum,* Biological Sciences, 1965, **9** (4).

Liddell, H. S.   Animal origins of anxiety. In M. L. Reymert (Ed.), *Feelings and emotions: the Mooseheart Symposium.* New York: McGraw-Hill, 1950. Pp. 181–188.

Lorenz, K. Z.   *King Solomon's ring.* New York: Crowell, 1952.

Maier, N. R. F., and Schneirla, T. C.   *Principles of animal psychology.* (2nd ed.) New York: Dover, 1964.

Moltz, H.   Imprinting: empirical basis and theoretical significance. *Psychol. Bull.,* 1960, **57**, 291–314.

Moment, G. B.   *General Zoology.* Cambridge, Mass.: Riverside, 1958.

Moore, Ruth.   *Man, time and fossils.* New York: Knopf, 1963.

Moore, Ruth.   *Evolution.* Life Nature Library. New York: Time, 1964.

Morgan, C. L.   *Introduction to comparative psychology.* New York: Scribner's, 1894 (2nd ed., 1906).

Mowrer, O. H.   *Learning theory and the symbolic processes.* New York: Wiley, 1960.

Olds, J.   Pleasure centers in the brain. *Sci. Amer.,* 1956, **195** (4), 105–116.

Oparin, A. I.   *Life, its nature, origin and development* (trans. Ann Synge). New York: Academic, 1962.

Oparin, A. I.   *The origin of life.* Edinburgh and London: Oliver and Boyd, 1957.

Oparin, A. I.   *The origin of life* (trans. Sergius Morgulis). New York: Dover, 1953.

Ovsiankina, M.   Die Wiederaufname unterbrochener Handlungen. *Ps. Forsch,* 1928, **11** (302), 690.

Patton, R. A.   Abnormal behavior in animals. In C. P. Stone (Ed.). *Comparative psychology.* Englewood Cliffs, N. J.: Prentice-Hall, 1951. Pp. 471–472.

Penfield, W., and Roberts, L.   *Speech and brain mechanisms.* Princeton, N.J.: Princeton Univer. Press, 1959.

Pliny.   *Natural history,* III, Book VIII (trans. H. Rackham). Cambridge, Mass.: Harvard Univer. Press, 1947.

Romanes, G. J.   *Mental evolution in animals.* New York: Appleton-Century-Croft, 1884.

Romer, A. S. Phylogeny and behavior with special reference to vertebrate evolution. In Anne Roe and G. G. Simpson (Eds.) *Behavior and evolution.* New Haven, Conn.: Yale Univer. Press, 1958.

Scott, J. P. On the evolution of fighting behavior. *Science,* 1965, **148** (3671), 820–821. Rev. of *The natural history of aggression.* Carthy, J. D., and Ebling, F. J. (Eds.). New York: Academic, 1964.

Shapiro, M. M. Respondent salivary conditioning during operant lever pressing in dogs. *Science,* 1960, **132** (3427), 619–620.

Shapiro, M. M. Salivary conditioning in dogs during fixed-interval reinforcement contingent upon lever pressing. *J. exp. anal. Behav.,* 1961, **4** (4), 361–364.

Skinner, B. F. *The behavior of organisms.* New York: Appleton-Century-Crofts, 1938.

Skinner, B. F. Superstition in the pigeon. *J. exp. Psychol.,* 1948, **38,** 168–172.

Skinner, B. F. Pigeons in a pelican. *Amer. Psychol.,* 1960, **15,** 28–37.

Skinner, B. F. *Cumulative record.* New York: Appleton-Century-Crofts, 1961 (48).

Slijper, E. J. Whales. New York: Basic Books, 1958.

Southwick, C. H. (Ed.) *Primate social behavior.* Princeton, N.J.: Van Nostrand, 1963.

Tinbergen, N. *The study of instinct.* Oxford: Clarendon, 1951.

van Heel, W. H. D. Sound and cetacea. *Neth. Jour. Sea Research,* 1962, **1** (4), 407–507.

von Holst, E. Electrically controlled behavior. *Sci. Amer.,* March 1962, **206** (3), 50–59.

Warden, C. J., Jenkins, T. N., and Warner, L. H. *Comparative psychology.* New York: Ronald, 1935.

Watson, J. B. *Psychology from the standpoint of a behaviorist.* (2nd ed.), Philadelphia: Lippincott, 1924.

Woodworth, R. S. *Experimental psychology.* New York: Holt, 1938.

Young, O. R. A survey of general systems theory. *General Systems: Yearbook of the Society for General Systems.* 1964, **IX,** 61–80; The impact of general systems theory on political science, 1964, **IX,** 239–253.

Index